NEW IDEAS IN ART EDUCATION

CITY OF CARBONDALE

222 East Main   P. O. Box 849   Carbondale, Illinois 62901

618/549-5302   Office of Rat and Pest Control

September 9, 1971

Dr. James Sullivan
Art Department
Allyn Building
S.I.U.
Carbondale, IL 62901

Dear Dr. Sullivan,

Last year we made several presentations to course number 399 concerning the rat problem in the United States and Carbondale in particular. The presentations touch on all aspects of the problem, including the problems of proper garbage disposal, poisons and the history of rats.

Our presentations include an up-to-date slide presentation featuring scenes of local areas that students would be familiar with. We provide our own slide projector and screen for classrooms not so equiped.

We would like very much to offer our "show" to your students this year. If you feel that such a program would once again fit into your schedule please let us know.

Sincerely,

Thomas D. Bevirt,
Project Director

TDB/jj

This will be my 1st presentation to the art history seminar.

NEW IDEAS
IN ART EDUCATION

A Critical Anthology

Edited by Gregory Battcock

A Dutton  *Paperback*

NEW YORK
E. P. DUTTON & CO., INC.
1973

Published simultaneously in Canada by Clarke, Irwin & Company
Limited, Toronto and Vancouver.

SBN 0-525-47345-9

INDIVIDUAL COPYRIGHTS AND ACKNOWLEDGMENTS:

Serge Chermayeff: *The Shape of Humanism*. Reprinted from *Arts
in Society*, Vol. 8, No. 2 (Summer-Fall, 1971) by permission of the
author.

Les Levine: *The Great American Art Machine*. Reprinted from
Studio International (June, 1971) by permission of the author.

Ernest Mandel: *The Marxist Theory of Alienation*. Reprinted from
International Socialist Review, Vol. 31, No. 3 (May, 1970) by permission of the author.

Albert Eide Parr: *The Happy Habitat*. Reprinted from *The Journal
of Aesthetic Education*, Vol. 6, No. 3 (July, 1972) by permission of
the author.

Allan Kaprow: *The Education of the Un-Artist, Part I*. Reprinted
from *Art News*, Vol. 69, No. 10 (February, 1971) by permission of
the author.

Harold Rosenberg: *Educating Artists*. Reprinted from *The New
Yorker*, Vol. XLV, No. 13 (May 17, 1969) by permission of the
author and editor. Copyright © 1969 The New Yorker Magazine,
Inc.

Patricia Sloan: *Teaching Art History in the Community College*.
Printed by permission of the author.

Irving Sandler: *New Ways of Teaching Art History*. Printed by
permission of the author.

Carol Duncan: *Teaching the Rich*. Printed by permission of the
author.

Ernesto J. Ruíz de la Mata: *The Art Critic as a Pedagogue*. Printed
by permission of the author.

Howard Conant: *Season of Decline*. Printed by permission of the
author.

Allen Leepa: *Art and Self: The Morphology of Teaching Art*.
Printed by permission of the author.

Vincent Lanier: *Art and the Disadvantaged*. Reprinted from *Art
Education*, Vol. 23, No. 9 (December, 1970) by permission of the
author.

Irving Kaufman: *Art Education: In and Out of School.* Reprinted from *The Wisconsin Monographs of Visual Arts Education,* No. 2 (Spring, 1971) by permission of the author.

Cindy Nemser: *Interview with an Anonymous Artist.* Reprinted from *Art Education* (January, 1970) by permission of the author. *Interview with Scott Free* printed by permission of the author.

James Sullivan: *Perceptarium.* Printed by permission of the author.

Al Hurwitz: *Experiment in Intermedia.* Reprinted from *Art Education* (March, 1970) by permission of the author.

Frederick M. Logan: *Environmental Aesthetics for Teachers of Art.* Reprinted from *Art Education,* Vol. 23, No. 7 (October, 1970) by permission of the author.

GREGORY BATTCOCK is editor of several anthologies of criticism in the fine arts, including *The New Art, Minimal Art, The New American Cinema,* and *The New Music.* He is Special Correspondent for *Arts Magazine* and New York Correspondent for *Art and Artists.* Critical essays by Mr. Battcock have been published in *Art in America, Domus,* and *The Art Journal.* He teaches at William Paterson College in New Jersey and is general editor of the Dutton series called "Documents in Modern Art Criticism."

CONTENTS

. . . .

INTRODUCTION   ix

PART ONE: Information and the Individual   1
   Serge Chermayeff: The Shape of Humanism   3
   Les Levine: The Great American Art Machine   11
   Ernest Mandel: The Marxist Theory of Alienation   29
   Albert Eide Parr: The Happy Habitat   52

PART TWO: Education for the Artist   71
   Allan Kaprow: The Education of the Un-Artist, Part I   73
   Harold Rosenberg: Educating Artists   91

PART THREE: Art History in College   103
   Patricia Sloan: Teaching Art History in the
     Community College   105
   Irving Sandler: New Ways of Teaching Art History   117
   Carol Duncan: Teaching the Rich   128
   Ernesto J. Ruíz de la Mata: The Art Critic as a
     Pedagogue   141

PART FOUR: Art Education: Criticisms   147
   Howard Conant: Season of Decline   149
   Allen Leepa: Art and Self: The Morphology of
     Teaching Art   171
   Vincent Lanier: Art and the Disadvantaged   181
   Irving Kaufman: Art Educator: In and Out of School · 203

Cindy Nemser: Two Interviews: Interview with an
Anonymous Artist and Interview with Scott Free   223

PART FIVE: Experiment and Proposal   235

James Sullivan: Perceptarium   237

Al Hurwitz: Experiment in Intermedia   255

Frederick M. Logan: Environmental Aesthetics for
Teachers of Art   266

Gregory Battcock: An Experiment with Art in
Education   279

INTRODUCTION

. . . .

Extraordinary changes have occurred in the artmaking process as well as in the nature of artworks during the past decade. Principles concerning the quality, the cultural function, and the materials of art have been defied by many contemporary artists. Not only do we find that such formerly important subjects as color, composition, drawing, and design have been rejected or completely reinterpreted; we also discover that such qualities as self-expression, individuality, originality, and creativity are no longer automatically as basic to art as we thought them to be. One result of this sweeping reorientation on the part of art and artists is that many standard procedures and goals in art education need to be reexamined. In the course of such reexamination we may discover that many values have become unimportant. They will have to be discarded; some, indeed, are already in the process of being replaced.

The need in art education for a total readjustment to change is particularly evident in the area of practical design. For example, many of us are no longer so eager to applaud a well-designed object merely because it satisfies established technical and aesthetic criteria. Within the past several years a new way of thinking about design has emerged; in a broad sense, the new philosophy seems to be unconcerned with the appearance of things. What may be more important than the usual pictorial elements such as style and beautification are considerations that lean toward placement, relationships between objects, and relationships between objects and people. As one contributor to this book notes ". . . we need the enchantment of spaces charmingly defined on the human scale." [1] In short, what has become of paramount importance in design today is the idea and theory of visual phenomena and relationships, and added to this is their effect upon one's behavior and spirit.

Many new critics, historians, educators, and artists are ill at ease with popular academic and institutional efforts within art. They seem, in the main, to be engaged in a search for new criteria ". . . as art defects and departs into strange territories leaving the old stand-by criteria to rule an eroding plain." [2] Yet the search for new criteria is not motivated exclusively by a desire to alleviate the connoisseur's dilemma. It is, in the main, an effort rather to identify criteria that will be less dictatorial and precise. They will not be "formula" criteria either. Instead, they will allow for the legitimate application, in art-making and understanding, of once-unthinkable viewpoints and standards.,

One immediate result for art is that visual imagery will be relieved of its common subordination to process. The criteria for artmaking must now be sought within the new disciplines; they will provide the content and energy for new art. Today's artist, art educator, and critic will find aesthetic stimulation *not* in art but outside of it. The subject of art will cease to be art.

This book presents essays by art critics, art educators, art historians, artists, and one director emeritus of the American Museum of Natural History, that are unique in the way they prepare the groundwork for the intro-

[1] See "The Happy Habitat" by Albert Eide Parr.
[2] Leo Steinberg, *Other Criteria* (New York: Oxford University Press, 1972).

duction of a radically new theoretical and practical approach for art education. They address the method, the content, and the goals of art education with considerable criticism. Though the documents printed here represent diverse viewpoints, what they generally have in common is a negative attitude toward the usual practices and ambitions of art education taught in today's schools and colleges.

The majority of the contributors to this book appear to favor a theory of art education that goes far beyond the mere manufacture and appreciation of decorative objects and designs. Most of the contributors view the various areas of art education and scholarship as a broad communicative system that is inseparable from social, urban, and global conditions. Thus what binds them together (other than glue) is that they either reject or ignore the usual "dilemmas" in art education that revolve around such time-honored issues as creativity, motivation, talent, and mastery of technique.

The reader should then be warned. For the most part, the unconventional theoretical (and pragmatic) viewpoints introduced here do not concern themselves with some of the most basic problems in art education, appreciation, and teaching. Nor do the several areas of art education—such as college training for artists, art experiences for elementary school children, art-education techniques for teachers, etc.—receive more than surface attention. What is important is the criticism of the unquestioning following of standard practice. In some areas alternatives are proposed.

The central purpose of this volume is to sow seeds of suspicion. Prevailing practices should be vigorously examined and reexamined, for the field of art education seems to be slipping backward as reality in art and the desperate need for dramatic restructuring of the visual environment become increasingly removed from the influence of art institutions. As many of the writers in the book point out, the broad and complex field of art education possesses enormous potential for the invention and application of viable, positive alternatives. It remains to be seen whether or not they will be effectively tapped.

These essays are designed to present ideas, commentary, and provocation for people in art communication: art educators, students, art critics, cultural historians, artists, and art historians. However, it has been suggested that it may be unreasonable to expect educators, critics, historians, and connoisseurs to anticipate, if not encourage, major shifts in the relatively stagnant area of art communication. Such specialists must feel a growing sense of alienation from contemporary artistic developments; so much so that it frequently becomes possible to turn away from such developments in favor of more familiar scholarship. Similarly, it has been pointed out that by the very nature of their professions and learning, such specialists prefer to cope with art that remains within established patterns conforming to definite specializations, rigid disciplines, and painstakingly acquired expertise. Rejection of old and implementation of new goals is frequently a painful exercise. Since the specialists appear to have the most to lose in the advent of great change, why then should we encourage such change?

In one direction, the new criteria, together with the initiative and energy for change, will be provided from areas outside of art itself. We may look to the fields of urban planning, environmental studies, television, and behavioral science to name some possibilities. Or, possibly, the required initiative may come from within the art-education establishment itself. Many art specialists will detect, within the tradition of art, ample precedent in the pattern of negation that surfaces from time to time to claim distinctly new priorities and criteria. We find such a wave occurring in late nineteenth-century France; in Siena in the Duecento; and, of course, in New York School Abstract Expressionism. The most likely course, however, will necessarily combine both possibilities. It will result in an infusion of ideas from outside of art with a willingness, or a climate, for rejection of art within art.

It is the editor's hope that the reader will find these articles enjoyable and thought provoking. They do not offer many specific answers. Occasionally they are extreme in their criticism. Mainly, they illustrate the need for more new ideas in a field that has been somewhat short of them. One educator, when asked to contribute an article to a book called *New Ideas in Art Education,* remarked: "I didn't know there were any!" As these essays prove, there are a great many. The editor was amazed to discover so much thought designed to invigorate the field. It remained to bring it all together.

GREGORY BATTCOCK

Part One

. . . .

INFORMATION
AND
THE INDIVIDUAL

THE SHAPE OF HUMANISM *

Serge Chermayeff

. . . .

Two frequent goals in art education—that there be more of it, and that it aspire to a recognized goal of excellence—are among many standard educational and cultural values that Serge Chermayeff questions in this essay, when he notes: "The University . . . has the marked capacity to remove art from the context of mystique . . . and to put the creative process as a whole in its proper perspective as a human activity that is carried on at different levels of excellence."

The author points out: "We have to accept the fact that reality is a process of living development, change, and growth and that the notion of completion is a mortuary concept." However reality isn't always recognized. One result, in America, is that: "Children are totally protected from any contact with reality with the result that they become unbearable and unteachable . . ." Yet another example of a "fragmented culture" is that ". . . we systematically exclude every single group that

* Reprinted from *Arts in Society*, Vol. 8, No. 2 (Summer–Fall, 1971).

*does not conform to the established norms
and institutions."*

*Chermayeff calls for ". . . great priorities in
design" that might, eventually provide for
"mixing places" because "It is important that
we continually encounter persons of varying
culture, intellectual preoccupation, and emotional makeup and color."*

*Today's designer must be ". . . multidi-
mensional . . . and totally comprehensive.
. . . a commitment to design public places
that will be rewarding, rich containers for
life."*

*Serge Chermayeff is Professor Emeritus, De-
partment of Architecture, Yale University, and
Fellow of the Royal Institute of British Architects, and the author of* Shape of Community:
Realization of Human Potential.

· · · · · · · · · · · · · · · · · ·

I think we are all perfectly conscious of being in a transition period. Though everybody describes the accompanying aches and pains in different ways, for the sake
of argument I think one could say that what is really
happening to us at the moment is that we are moving
away from a concept of the world that assumes rather
simple things and simple ways of doing things and we
are now nervously beginning to accept the sense of complexity that has suddenly been revealed to us—a complexity that governs all forms of life, including man. We
do not like the new view. It makes us uneasy.

For years we have been prone to describe human beings through the use of simplistic, mechanistic analogies,
assuming, for example, that since each member of the
species had a similar circulatory, digestive, and nervous

system, that we were all governed by a constant set of factors. But it is now apparent that that view did not tell us much about the real nature of individuals, who are infinitely variable, not only in time and space, but within their own beings. Fingerprints have for a long time suggested the fact of personal variability, but now we also have the evidence of voice prints further to highlight our sense of strangeness to one another—the strangeness we all now feel even amidst the intimacy of the family breakfast table.

So we have to get used to the idea that we are living in a very complex world, one constantly undergoing an evolutionary process. We no longer can take it for granted that everything is going to be exactly the same from the moment of birth to the moment of one's convenient disposal. We have to accept the fact that reality is a process of living development, change, and growth, and that the notion of completion is a mortuary concept.

Though the significance of change is still largely ignored, it has become the most vital aspect of our life. Through the acceleration of change, we and our society are continually becoming quite different. An important fact that we are still failing to grasp is that a qualitative change is the inevitable by-product of quantitative increase. For years we have been in the ridiculous trap of believing that more was always better. We were quantity-minded consumers in our approach to practically all problems—with the result that we now find ourselves trapped in this environmental mess.

The deteriorating environment has actually two natures: that which exists outside human endeavor but which is becoming more and more modified by our interference with it, and that which is man-made. The latter has now become more powerful and pervasive than nature itself. At the same time both are moving toward an indissolvable kind of duality. We can no longer step aside when we have made a mistake and hope that the jungle will cover up the error. We just have nowhere to go. Our mistakes haunt us and everything that we pollute or interfere with remains a constant reminder of our persistent folly, some of which has reached a point of no return.

To summarize the nature of my concern and commitment, it has become very obvious that things are, indeed, complex and not simple and that this complexity is something of which we have to become masters.

I do not think there is any question in anybody's mind that technological development has extended the range of our ability to deal with complexity. For example, the telescope and microscope have infinitely broadened our natural capacity to see, the automobile and airplane our natural mobility. But we have also actually extended the whole of our nervous system through the new processes and methods of cybernetics. For the first time we have the necessary tools to make all problems manageable in terms of analysis and measurement. This is perhaps the most significant development that has ever been witnessed in history.

Our new technological capacity to deal with complexity can also be viewed as potentially a vastly increased creative capacity for a man, in a new sense. Since the arts have always dealt fundamentally with complexity, one presumes that the artists are now challenged to move into an expanded role. But it is most difficult to define what that role might be. We do not yet clearly know how the artist operates. We do know that he comes by all sorts of strange quantum jumps to solutions that are as good as or sometimes better than the logical structures of lesser men. But we have not yet learned how to measure this capacity or how to encourage its flourishing. Certainly it seems evident that we can no longer indulge our sense of aestheticism, a practice that normally is a symptom of uneasiness and escape.

Practicing creative minds do not discuss the nature of excellence and the perfection of their acts. They just look at them. I have had any number of painters come to my house (which I am happy to say is filled with paintings from some rather distinguished people—the collected loot of a long life) who never look around at the paintings. These are pseudovisual people. Instead they talk about themselves. Then I know I am not talking to an artist and that I shall never have to invite him to my house again. There are these kind of litmus-paper tests that I think can be reasonably applied in considering the question of the role of the artist.

Now that we can tackle complexity as a whole, we can say that the past is not just history but an ever present component of the present, and that the future is not something in a crystal ball (to be sneered at) but the predictable obvious that is just as much part and parcel of the present as the past. So what we are now searching for in every act, and particularly when we are designing environments, is some kind of vision of a new symbiosis. It is this symbiosis that we are obviously searching for— not only between us and what we still think of as nature, but between us and other men. This is our challenge.

No matter who plans what or where the result has its reverberation in the Pacific, in Africa, Latin America, Russia, China, or any other place you would like to think of as physical or political, economic, technological entities. In fact, what we are seeking is a symbiosis for the human species, one global in its nature, effect, and purpose.

We do not yet realize that when we say let us have more of something that appears very seductive, that more is going to become either better or worse. And when it becomes worse the result is threatening and may even mean death and destruction. I do not think we have to wait now for a nuclear holocaust to destroy our humanity. All we have to do is to continue to build cities as we have in the past—thoughtlessly.

Now we know that technology has its own pace and moves absolutely independently of any institutional or cultural patterns. It spins off way ahead of institutional adjustment to the new realities. Most of our problems really result from the fantastic disparity between technological growth and our institutional reaction. So it is institutions that you must finally battle and not technology, which is relatively simple and has its own logic and inevitable process of advance. Actually the lag between the two is lengthening, and if you were to draw a graph showing the current relationship you would find that we have reached a point of no return. Now the technological effect digs right down into our biophysical, pyschological, evolutionary pattern, which we always took for granted as being eternal, untouchable—a kind of framework within which we could conveniently maneuver and escape destruction. We cannot escape the consequences of our acts anymore. We are undermining the very roots of our being, the very roots, if you like, of our humanity.

In Galbraithian terms our society is now a "technostructure." This is a culture in which everything interacts. It is for that reason that we have to build new bridges between diverse sets of understanding. We can no longer afford to draw the line between intuition and intellect, but must develop tools and media that will be shared by the scientist and artist alike.

Because of its resources and because of its objective stance, the university has an apt role in developing our capacity to denote and deal with complexity. It can not only help forge links between the various methods and mechanics of inquiry but it has the marked capacity to remove art from the context of mystique or fashion, and to put the creative process as a whole in its proper perspective as a human activity that is carried on at different levels of excellence. Most people are not creative because they have never been given an opportunity to exercise their talents. There are any number of situations today in which we lose excellence of all sorts simply because we have not provided ample opportunity for it to exercise itself in the company of its peers.

In America we have a peculiarly fragmented culture. Children are totally protected from any contact with reality with the result that they become unbearable and unteachable. The old are considered to have lived beyond their usefulness when their reactions are slower and we forbid them the great "open sesame" of our culture, the driving license. But we do more than neglect our children and our old people; we systematically exclude every single group that does not conform to the established norms and institutions.

There are no mixing places in our culture. The designing of the environmental process must include the making of mixing places—public places where young and old, middle-aged and adolescent, will find themselves as a matter of daily necessity and be able to observe how humanity behaves at different stages of its development. It is important that we continually encounter persons of varying culture, intellectual preoccupation, and emotional makeup and color.

What I am talking about, of course, are the great priorities in design—compassion for others, human concern, awareness of the condition of *all* men. Indeed, it particularly behooves us to become sensitive to the needs and aspirations of those we don't know, because they may very well become the very catalysts we need in order to transform ourselves.

As he approaches the now enlarged and complex societal vision of environment, the designer assumes multiple responsibilities, social and moral as well as technical. Similarly, his commitment must be multidimensional, broad-based, and totally comprehensive. It is a commitment to design public places that will be rewarding, rich containers for life; places where man in balanced measure meets strangeness and adventure as well as reassurance and the expected; places of concourse, of mix and the maximization of human experience; complementary places offering choices between apparently contradictory opposites; places to induce receptivity to new ideas: all conceived as part of the kind of open system essential to human evolution.

Simplistic scientistic answers or arty attitudes will no longer do. If we follow Bertrand Russell's advice to "remember your humanity and forget all the rest," then we can be assured, in the words of Eric Gill, that "beauty will look after herself."

THE GREAT AMERICAN
ART MACHINE *

Les Levine

. . . .

*In the conclusion to this article, Les Levine
declares: "Art now reads out as social software: information." Levine believes that, ultimately, the artist will cease to exist as a separate, heroic figure—once we realize that the
purpose of art is to influence software.*

*The author comes to this conclusion through
extensive and illuminating examination of
many contemporary communicative phenomena that, combined, result in "the information
fall-out." Among those information factors he
discusses are: television commercials, programming, advertising, technology, media society,
Charles Manson, privacy, Telex, computers,
and art. His ideas complement notions proposed by several philosophers and critics, including Buckminster Fuller and Herbert Marcuse. And, like Marshall McLuhan before him,
Levine, no doubt, would agree that ". . . by
going to school (the child) interrupts his education."*

* First published as "The Information Fall-Out" in *Studio International* (June, 1971).

Les Levine (left) discusses I.R.A. press conference with Paddy Kennedy, Republican Labour Member of Parliament for Belfast Central (March, 1972).

*Les Levine has had over sixty one-man shows
in Canada, the United States, and abroad. He
publishes an infrequent newspaper called* Culture Hero *and is president of the Museum of
Mott Art, Inc., which he founded. He claims
to have coined the word "software" in art
terms, which became the subject of an exhibition at the Jewish Museum in New York. Since
1969 he has been working with the art world
as a social system rather than producing objects
for use by that same system.*

. . . .

Most of the works that are concerned with information
are using media as a form of "evidence-creating." The
photographs or documents act pretty much in the way
they are used in the courtroom. They are presented to
make it absolutely clear that such and such a thing has
occurred. They are not to be considered for their particular aesthetic quality. They're merely brought into
the courtroom as a form of circumstantial evidence to
prove that in fact a specific thing has occurred, and this
is the way it looked when it did occur. The medium, in
most of these works, is information.

The best informational works are those that abdicate
completely any aesthetic authority, make no judgment
about the kind of information, but merely present it as
a logical vacuum. In a systematic society, when a situation has no logic (a logical vacuum), immediately logic
rushes in to fill it. If something is not called by a particular name, immediately the information sources will put
a name on it. Because we are a systematic society, we
cannot live under circumstances that do not have a system.
Therefore, we apply a system whether it be the wrong
one or not. The importance of the artist maintaining the

position that abdicates aesthetic position, or aesthetic authority, is that aesthetic authority is not "positive" to a socially supportive environment, because it generally tends to say simply, "You don't know what I'm doing. You don't understand this. If you could understand, you would be on the same intelligence level. I'm telling you this is something you should aspire to." If the artist abdicates aesthetic authority, he allows the work to be whatever the viewer wants it to be, to be a success or a failure on his level. And it doesn't matter whether it is a success or a failure, because the activity of the viewer dealing with it offers him enough support anyway. *The artist is now dealing with environmental energy.*

Television commercials are the real programming of television. The programs are basically commercials for the network. A commercial that is short works better than one that is long. A commercial that is long is an apology. So the information is somewhat dissipated. One advertisement basically says, "We have a product and we want to sell it." The second advertisement says, "We have a product and we haven't sold it." The third says, "We have a product and we still haven't sold it." The fourth says, "We're going to keep at this until we sell it." And the fifth and sixth, and so on, continually remind you of the previous advertisement rather than the product. People who advertise every day are telling you, "We advertise more": the idea, of course, being that if we advertise more, we have the money, we have the power. The everyday advertisers are not selling the product, they are selling themselves. A company that advertises once or twice is saying to the public that they need them as a customer, and a company that advertises a lot is saying, "We don't need you as a customer because we're very powerful."

The reason long television commercials don't work as well as short ones has to do with the nature of television.

The viewer is watching the program and if he is not getting information at a one-to-one ratio, he tends to go to sleep. In other words, as soon as he's got the information, and it is not immediately changed to another piece of information, it becomes softer and softer all the time until it gradually dulls in his mind. Whereas if the information is changed quickly, it acts more or less like a strobe light, which is constantly shaking him up all the time.

The idea that we have any choice whatsoever, in a completely technological environment, is pretty ridiculous; we only assume we make a choice. However, most of the choices that we make are merely selections taken out of a precoded number of choices that society has already made for us. The society is clearly *pre-choiced*. Relative to this idea, these selections have nothing to do with a moral or religious position. Previous to moral-ethical beliefs man believed that choices were quantitative. A farmer's crop was a good crop because it was a large crop, and a bad crop because it was small. Then with the advent of "religious teaching" it was made clear that it would be possible to consider something that was small as being good and something that was large as being bad: morality as it relates to choice. Now, continuing on this the idea of aesthetics as it relates to religion and morality, aesthetic activity, such as artmaking, then became a "moral activity." The idea of making good art became, in the religious sense, moral, and making bad art, in the religious sense, immoral. However, we now have passed to a state where choices are no longer relative to morality. The media and technology have made clear that everybody in a democratic society has a right to say for himself, "This is good or bad for me, and this is what I want, and this is what I don't want. What I want and what I don't want are decided by society anyway." Therefore it's no longer a moral issue. If you decide that it is a moral issue, then there are certain groups of people who are doing the right thing and there are certain people who are doing the wrong thing, relative to aesthetics. We have a society in which it is possible for everybody to make art. That fact is more interesting than any particular moral or aesthetic code that you might apply to art.

We have created a media society. Things are done for the effect that they will have in the media, rather than the effect they have on the environment. It's assumed that the effect in the media will automatically affect the socioeconomic environment. Hence, the court trials of Abbie Hoffman create an environmental theatrical work, which in effect is turned into a novel. So that the overall effect is that the government, the courtroom, the lawyers, the defendants, etc., are engaged in a piece of media theatre. This is what Jerry Rubin calls the "Do It" generation. You do something because the doing of it will have information fallout and burn-off, which then will be assessed logically by the society. *The logic of the activity will be the fact that it has been done.*

Then Charles Manson, who so desperately wants to become part of the media environment (allegedly), slaughters eight people. This dire destructive crime, which has various witchcraft overtones, is horrible in its scope. However, when we analyze it more closely, Manson very quickly becomes a superstar of the media. He becomes a charismatic character of unbelievably celebrated proportions; he is sought after by every newspaper and network in the country for interviews; he's on the front page of every newspaper and magazine; he's become a historical figure overnight. For Manson to "make it" as a rock-and-roll star was one way of leading him into the media, of receiving great adulation from the press, etc. But then, deciding to kill all these people, in order to achieve fame, is one of the nightmares of the media generation. This negative action is another one of those "Do It" things. And it is even further extended when Richard Nixon, who understands very clearly the enormous energy the activity has, no matter how dire it may be, decides it is necessary for him to plug into that energy (by saying that Manson is guilty), the same way a politician decides it's necessary to plug into the pollution problem, the war in Vietnam, urban renewal, or any other charismatic piece of energy in the media. Manson has taken media paranoia to the ultimate point of destruction. The outcome of the situation is: What are eight lives in order to make a "software superstar" of national proportions? Would a television network be prepared to sacrifice eight lives for a program that would constantly get them, over a period of a year, sixty million viewers?

Relative to this, we have the movie *Woodstock* in which the people went to Woodstock to hear music and to be together. Actually they paid to participate in the production of a movie. The Woodstock Festival occurred solely to make a movie. The movie relates in the way the photographs, as evidence, relate in information art. The movie is merely evidence that this festival occurred.

Instead of using closed-format approaches to writing scripts, which in some way will represent the cultural operative trust of society, we merely take the operative trust directly and use that as a working model of itself and present that as the work. We're looking at a direct piece of life, which has been presented as art. Instead of taking a work of art, which if it were translated would present an aspect of life or decode as a particular concern, we merely take the direct working situation and present it (documented) as the work. This is *Woodstock,* this is Manson, this is Hoffman, this is information art. Now we must achieve motivation retrospectively: *we look backward to see the effect of what we have done and that becomes our reason for doing it.*

Whatever anybody says in the media, always happens. If someone on television says the economy is in bad condition, the economy will be bad the moment after he has said it. Anything that stands out on the media as negative at a given moment will become positive in a very short time. The media accelerates its own information.

Through information processing, a negative logic occurs. What you attempt to give power will reject power; an attempt to detract power will immediately attract power, like a negative energy system. It is not possible to say something is bad (or good) because the viewers see that *you* are *telling* them that it's good (or bad). Therefore, they do not believe you. Trying to undermine something on television works in absolute reverse. For example, commercials to stop smoking tell us how dangerous it can be to our health, etc. They also, remind us that this is a very enjoyable habit, and it would be nice to be smoking right now. When C.B.S. covers up Abbie Hoffman's face on television because he is wearing an American flag shirt, the viewers see that they are putting Hoffman down, and therefore automatically put him up higher than before.

Talking about a problem in the media is almost the same thing as solving the problem. People used to say: "Everything will be okay, so long as we keep the dialogue going." This bred the mediocre intellectual who thought there was nothing more to do except be semantic about the problem, never actually considering what should be done. So that the consideration in itself became the problem, and the semantics with it became the problem, more than the real "problem."

Information, that is in the environment, always relates to other kinds of information. The Pollution Control Board virtually means that "x" number of people will get a job in the United States Government. Before that it was urban renewal. These things are supported by politicians because they provide a large amount of political patronage. Government sees art as a way to pretty up the environment.

The media refused to recognize any subtleties in art whatsoever because they transform art into information. In other words, Earth art, Electronic art, abstract art, Pop art and so on. The practitioners of these styles in art attack the media for being nothing more than commercial. It would be impossible for any style to exist as a real entity without the media. "Great American Art from 1940–1970": it was not that when the museum said it was; it was that when the media had decided that that's what it was.

In information processing, there is always a key phrase that simplifies: Impressionism, out-of-focus images; Abstract Expressionism, slopping around in paint; Pop art, big popular images that we consider banal; Earth art, holes in the ground. Light art is anything that has light bulbs; Electronic art is anything that flashes electrically. Although artists are appalled all the time by the way the media read art out, none of these movements would exist as a reality to the general population without the media. I think it is clear that Ad Reinhardt would not have been "Ad Reinhardt" without the media. The idea of the "black painting with nothing on it" (which is what most people in the media thought it was), as opposed to abstract painting, is the way the media established a man who abhorred the media.

"Great American Art from 1940–1970" was probably the last important show about hierarchical Western taste. It was the final stance in an approach to moralistic, aesthetic, and ethical art. The sad part about that situation was a curator expressing a lack of support for the artistic environment, at a time when the artistic environment needed support more than ever. It is a position that says,

A.I.R. by Les Levine from "Software" exhibition, The Jewish Museum, 1970.

"We will set up these idols at the cost of the rest of the art community, and who cares about the rest of the community if it's all crap anyway. Museums only want to show the good stuff." We have come to the point that showing the good stuff may in fact be good for only a small group of people and for a very large group of people it may act as a negative, nonsupporting system. The *"ideal"* in a postmoral, postconscious society is of little value.

Behaviors in our society occur because we have laws about them. The nature of the environment combined with the law clearly expresses what is possible and permissible within that environment. Whether we morally agree or disagree doesn't make too much difference.

The Museum of Modern Art's "Information" Exhibition, New York, 1970: the style of the show was photographic, while there was no style. While there were some eighty artists in the show, there were no artists in the show: no one stood out any more than another. Every movement previous, such as Pop, Op, Color Painting, always had its figures. In Pop, it would be Andy Warhol, Roy Lichtenstein, Claes Oldenburg, and a few others. In Color Painting, it would be Morris Louis, Kenneth Noland, and on down the line. In the "Information" Exhibition, it was clear that the only outstanding figure was the curator. The curator in this situation becomes the artist. We have a "Woodstock" situation at the Museum of Modern Art. All of these people are brought together to make this show under the authorship of the curator. The curator presents the media with a package.

The value of shows like this is, because they are so open, they tend to have no taste or choice position. Now having no taste or choice position is valuable because it is a supportive position. It supports the socioeconomics of the art community. So it is decided that, rather than make breakthroughs with artists who hit home runs, you give the overall scene a vehicle to work with, an open communication system. If you see a show with eighty or more people in it, all of the people dissipate into one person, the curator, and the people who are not in it stand out more than the people who are in it.

A careful selection was made so that none of the works would be outstanding. So none of the works could in fact actually exist as itself, as a personal element belonging to a particular artist. The ideas were all interchangeable with any of the other ideas in the show. It is clear now that ideas are not the property of anybody.

If you present the media with a show which apparently has no particular artist, they will make one of the people involved "the artist." And seeing that none of the artists stands out any more than others, the person who becomes "the artist" is the curator. The curator has made an artistic breakthrough. The curator has not only gathered the information, he has also made information: an artistic system that is supportive to the members of that system equally, rather than a system that supports particular figures in it and downgrades others.

The "Information" Exhibition came at a time when the Art Workers' Coalition had its many fights with the Museum of Modern Art. You can't take energy away from a powerful system without giving that system a considerable amount of energy. The Art Workers' Coalition was constantly attacking the Museum of Modern Art. The Museum of Modern Art then put on this giant "Information" Exhibition, which included all of its enemies. It became more powerful than it ever was before. It got rid of the idea that there are going to be any further personal breakthroughs in art. Because the idea of a personal breakthrough means that there is a particular set of facts or group of information or sensitivity to a situation that is particular to a specific person or group of people. However, it is impossible for any one person to have more facts than any other person now.

Shows of this type are presented as: This is the art of now. However, they are not the beginning of anything; they are the end. They show very clearly what art has been like in the past. In presenting the "Information" Exhibition, the museum made it virtually impossible for any artist of integrity to continue making pieces about information. Many people will say that the effect of this show was to demythologize art. I don't think they demythologize art. They put art in line with the social conditions.

There are two kinds of software: one is the very technical term, which is something a computer programmer needs to know; and the other is social software, which refers to the kinds of information in the environment that make us behave the way we do. The media environment is telling your brain how to operate; it is telling your body how to operate; it is telling you how to behave, what to look like, what to desire, what to look at, what to care about, what not to care about, what to be politically in favor of, what morally would be wrong, what would taste good, what doesn't taste good. In an environment that is constantly telling its inhabitants all these things, there is no such thing as individualism or personal property. If things become important to the general environment, the general environment will own them, and the individual will not. So the idea that the collector owns the artist's work is merely a hangover from a period in history when everyone viewed everything as property. The artist's work, whether it is owned by a collector or a museum, is always his work; it always will be owned by him no matter who has it in his possession. To assume we are individuals is very much beside the point. Of course, one could say, "I want that automobile there in red, with white-walled tires, and an air conditioner, etc."

But you have to take into consideration that the company who makes that automobile has done market research to find out that someone who looks pretty much like you, who earns about the amount of money that you do, who wears the same clothes, who lives in the same kind of house, who has the number of children that you have, who is related to the number of people that you are, who vacations in the place that you vacation, who goes to see the movies that you go to, etc., will come in and say, "I want that car in this color with white walls." Our culture gives people an illusion of choice.

This tendency to be constantly involved in the idea of individual choices stems from the computer, unless you interact in a reasonably passive way.

Information has affected law. A smart lawyer realizes that evidence that is passed across an information retrieval system, such as television or newspaper, is just as valuable as evidence that is presented in court. So what is occurring in the courtroom now is a direct reflection of what occurs in the media. It is often possible actually to lose a case in a courtroom, but win it in the media. If it is won in the media, it will be reversed in the courtroom. There is no way of un-knowing information. In a society that is addicted to information, it is extremely dangerous not to put out information. In a society that demands to know everything, the man who remains quiet is guilty.

Now privacy is redundant; privacy only works in a society that is technically private. It is possible for the government to spy on a citizen at any time. It is possible for one firm to spy on another firm. If you live in a society that does not permit privacy, trying to be private is foolish. If you have sex in your living room, it shouldn't matter if everybody in the world can see you. Because if they wanted to, they could. Privacy becomes one-sided when you resist it. If you don't resist, then you become part of the working environment. The correct organic cell in the correct organic environment. You take the same attitude toward the government that they take toward you.

Now people say that computers are dehumanizing us; that there are too many machines. There are even people who blame the war in Vietnam on computers. Very few people have had any firsthand use of computers as an information retrieval system, as a surrogate brain, as an outside intelligence support, as a form of artificial thinking. We must realize that if everybody has computers, then it becomes possible for everybody to talk to everybody else. If you have a Telex terminal and you want to say, "Screw you" on that terminal, everybody who owns a Telex terminal will get a printout saying, "Screw you." So that although companies do have the possibility to control you, if you are hooked into them you have the possibility to control back. Once we all have technological access, then we can talk to one another. The computer is going to bring about a new era of primitivism in art. The computer will in fact be the new folk art.

In a city, where people have answering services, instead of talking to people directly, the technology talks to the technology. You phone a person, his answering service answers. You leave a message. He phones you back and your answering service answers. The technology is making the decision and the people are sitting about on the sidelines. One computer is talking to another computer. One telephone is talking to another telephone. One television is talking to another television. Humans are merely looking at it once in a while to see what the result of all this activity is and deciding what they should do with it.

Technology has had a greater effect on the cultural thrust than art. Technology has created technological man. It has created political change. It has created aesthetic change. It has created many levels of things that we thought art would. Probably the greatest reason that technology has taken over from art is because art was always technology anyway. The art of the cave painter was a technological art. It was an art of how to do it, how to image the society, how to present society with a working model of itself that would in fact be a "conceptual tool," a valuable and useful device for the shaping of that society. Now we are coming back technologically to cave painting. We're now at a point where technology can present us with a working model of ourselves.

It is important that we expand the technological environment into a completely biotechnology environment so that we are interconnected very directly with the technology and that we can plug into any area of thinking to create a support system between one another. It is true that we are further apart ideologically than ever before in the world. It is also true that we are closer together than we have ever been.

Where does the art collector fit in? Apart from gathering objects to surround him, which give him a certain sense of place or personal environment, it's also true that collecting art has been a way of socially identifying oneself. The sophisticate now realizes that having a number of paintings on his wall is not going to increase his image to very many people. Buying works of art today would have little value or importance; everybody can buy everything anyway. There are no rich people, only middle-class people. The rich merely have more "middle class."

So the artist will have to create a personal publicity system for the collector. He will have to identify these people to the society. So he has to decide that these people will become media packages. He will package these people in such a manner that they will become information for society. The problem of collecting art objects is that the information reads out more about having money and power than it does about being aesthetically involved or concerned with art. Therefore, if one does have money and power, there is very little value in buying art because it's going to create bad information. Money and power represent personal politics at a time when everyone is trying to get to a broader intersupportive system. The only step left now would be for the collector to become an artist. He must be directly involved in art production. He could do it by selecting various groups of art and showing them in a similar way to that in which the curator of the Museum of Modern Art put on the "Information" Exhibition, or he could begin to make art that expresses the kind of person that he is, in the kind of environment that he finds himself. Museums will probably undergo an enormously difficult period; it will become evident to them that there will be an enormous increased production from artists. And the collection of this production will cause real estate problems, will cause economic problems, and will also cause political problems. What it will probably be important for museums to be doing within the next few years will be bringing in the various underprivileged social groups in our society. Presenting the museum as a community cultural laboratory rather than as a place that sets up high standards and aesthetics.

The absurdity of formal art criticism is that it is pretty much umbilical to collecting. Formal art criticism must be judged as organized power. For all that formal art criticism hates commercialism, it always acts as a very straight commercial for the art it's talking about. In formal criticism when you say, "Something is good," you're saying, "buy it." When you say, "It is bad," you're saying, "do not buy it." So formal art criticism will find itself with the same problem that the collector finds himself in. People do not want to be told constantly what their taste should be anymore. Good taste, at this time, in a technological democracy, ends up as nothing more than taste prejudice. Expressing aesthetic authority over another human being is arrogant.

The artist must, without question, abdicate. He must realize that his work should not contain authority. It must in fact have the capability to succeed or fail as the viewer wants it. Thereby being much more supportive to the viewer. It must, in fact, be completely devoid of logic. The logical vacuum must be there so that the viewer applies his own logic to it and the work in fact makes itself before the viewer's eyes. So that it becomes a direct reflection of the viewer's consciousness, logic, morals, and ethics. The work should act as a feedback mechanism to his own working model.

Once you have information about something, there is no need to do it. The one thing that so-called Do It activities, such as *Woodstock,* make absolutely clear, in information terms, is that you do it to get the information. That if you have the information, you don't do it because having the information means it's been done. So what we would have in art is a series of "doing it" that would create information. Television is pretty much like art in this situation. The only things that occur that are of interest to most people are commercials, sports events, and newscasts. We will have to get all the people watching television on television so that everyone's watching himself and everyone else.

What we are seeing now is a series of works that are made for the reason that they can be turned into media. Art now reads out as social software: information. Once we know that the purpose is to influence the social software we can do away with art and start influencing the social software directly. Beyond that the artist will probably dissolve, cease to exist in our society as a separate heroic figure.

THE MARXIST THEORY
OF ALIENATION *

Ernest Mandel

. . . .

*Mandel claims that the most tragic form of
alienation ". . . is the alienation of the capacity to communicate." For many artists, educators, and students today, this very same failure has drastically complicated issues and procedures in art education: for that reason his
essay appears in this volume.*

*Several contributors to this book have indi-
cated that the failure to communicate is a central issue in art education. James Sullivan
likens our society to the tombstone inscription
that reads ". . . all dressed up and no place
to go" and he complements Mandel's observations on the alienation of human labor when
he writes ". . . academia persists in fostering
the fabrication of objects in a social and intellectual vacuum." In a similar context, it is
worth considering Allan Kaprow's comment,
appearing elsewhere in this book ". . . that
the Southeast Asian theatre of war in Vietnam or the trial of the 'Chicago Eight,' while
indefensible, is better theatre than any play."*

* Reprinted from *International Socialist Review,* Vol. 31, No. 3
(May, 1970).

*Mandel, in expanding his theory of aliena-
tion, notes: "It is simply not true, as certain
existentialist philosophers contend, that man
has always been an essentially lonely human
being." And he believes that the majority of
members of our society are not yet in the situation of ". . . dialogues between people who
are incapable of understanding or listening to
other people."*

*Ernest Mandel, the Belgian philosopher, is
a distinguished analyst of socialist and Marxist
principles. His articles and books have been
translated into many languages and he is a
leading theorist of the New Left.*

. . . .

It was by studying Hegel that Marx first came across the
concept of alienation. But, oddly enough, it was not the
theory of alienated labor that he originally picked up
from Hegel's works. It was the alienation of man as a
citizen in his relationship with the state that became
the starting point of Marx's philosophical, political and
social thought.

The social contract theory maintained that in organized society the individual must forfeit a certain number
of individual rights to the state as the representative of
the collective interest of the community. Hegel especially
had developed this idea that was so strongly enunciated
by the theoreticians of the natural rights philosophy.
That also served as the starting point of Marx's critique
of Hegel and his beginning as a critical social thinker in
general.

Some small incidents which happened in the Rhine
province of western Germany around 1842/43 (the increase in the number of people who stole wood and the

intervention of the government against these people) led Marx to conclude that the state, which purports to represent the collective interest, instead represented the interests of only one part of the society, that is to say, those who own private property. Therefore the forfeiture of individual rights to that state represented a phenomenon of alienation: the loss of rights by people to institutions which were in reality hostile to them.

Starting from that political-philosophical platform, Marx, who in the meantime had been expelled from Germany and gone into exile in France, got in contact with the first socialist and workers organizations there and began to study economics, especially the classical writers of British political economy, the Adam Smith-Ricardo school. This was the background for Marx's first attempt in 1844 at a synthesis of philosophical and economic ideas in the so-called *Economic and Philosophic Manuscripts of 1844,* also called the *Parisian Manuscripts.* This was an attempt to integrate his ideas about labor in bourgeois society with ideas about the fate of man, man's position in history, and his existence on earth.

This initial youthful attempt at synthesis was carried out with very inadequate means. At that period Marx did not yet have a thorough knowledge of political economy; he had only started to acquaint himself with some of the basic notions of the classical school in political economy; and he had little direct or indirect experience with the modern industrial system. He would obtain all that only during the next ten years.

This unfinished early work was unknown for a very long time. It was first published in 1932, nearly one hundred years after it was written. Accordingly, much of the discussion which had been going on in economic as well as philosophic circles, about what he thought in his youth and how he arrived at a certain number of his basic concepts, was very much distorted by an ignorance of this specific landmark in his intellectual development.

Immature as parts of it might seem and are, especially the economic part, it nevertheless represents both a major turning point in Marx's intellectual development and in the intellectual history of mankind. Its importance, which I will try to explain, is linked with the concept of alienation.

Alienation is a very old idea that has religious origins and is almost as old as organized religion itself. It was taken over by nearly all the classical philosophical trends in the West as in the East. This concept turns around what one could call the tragic fate of man. Hegel, who was one of the greatest German philosophers, took over the idea from his predecessors but gave it a new slant and a new basis that denoted momentous progress. He did this by changing the foundation of that concept of the tragic fate of man from a vague anthropological and philosophical concept into a concept rooted in labor.

Hegel, before Marx, said that man is alienated because human labor is alienated. He gave two explanations for this general alienation of human labor. One is what he called the dialectics of need and labor. Human needs, he said, are always one step ahead of the available economic resources; men will therefore always be condemned to work very hard to fulfill unsatisfied needs. However, the attempt to equalize the organization of material resources with the necessity of satisfying all human needs is an impossible task, a goal that can never be attained. That was one aspect of what Hegel called alienated labor.

The other side of his philosophical analysis was a bit more complicated. It is summarized in a difficult word, the word "externalization" (*Entäusserung*). Though the term is complicated and sounds foreign, its content is easier to understand. Hegel meant by the philosophical concept of externalization the fact that every man who works, who produces something, really reproduces in his work an idea that he initially had in his head. Some of you might be astonished if I immediately add that Marx shared that opinion. You will find this same idea, that any work that man performs lives in his head before being realized in material reality, in the first chapter of *Capital*. Hegel, as well as Marx, thereby drew a basic distinction between men and, let us say, ants or other creatures that seem to be busily at work but do things purely by instinct. Man, on the other hand, first develops an idea about what he aims to do and then tries to realize that idea.

Hegel goes a step farther when he asks, what do we do in reality when we try to express, in material, what first lives in us as an idea? We inevitably separate ourselves from the product of our labor. Anything that we project out of ourselves, anything that we fabricate, anything that we produce, we project out of our own body and it becomes separated from us. It cannot remain as much part and parcel of our being as an idea that continues to live in our head. That was for Hegel the main, let us say, anthropological, definition of alienated labor. He therefore arrived at the conclusion that every and any kind of labor is alienated labor because in any society and under any conditions men will always be condemned to become separated from the products of their labor.

When Marx takes up these two definitions of alienated labor given by Hegel, he contradicts both of them. He says that the discrepancy between needs and material resources, the tension between needs and labor, is a limited one, conditioned by history. It is not true that man's needs can develop in an unlimited way or that the output of his collective labor will always remain inferior to these needs. He denies this most emphatically on the basis of a historical analysis. He especially rejects Hegel's idealistic identification of externalization with alienation. Marx says that when we separate ourselves from the product of our labor it does not necessarily follow that the product of our labor then oppresses us or that any material forces whatsoever turn against men. Such alienation is not the result of the projection of things out of our body as such, which first live in us as ideas and then take on a material existence as objects, as products of our labor.

Alienation results from a certain form of organization of society. More concretely, only in a society that is based on commodity production and only under the specific economic and social circumstances of a market economy can the objects that we project out of us when we produce acquire a socially oppressive existence of their own and be integrated in an economic and social mechanism that becomes oppressive and exploitative of human beings.

The tremendous advance in human thought that I referred to in this critique of Hegel consists in the fact that Marx rejects the idea of the alienation of labor as being an anthropological characteristic, that is, an inherent and ineradicable curse of mankind. He says that the alienation of labor is not bound to human existence in all places and for all future time. It is a specific result of specific forms of social and economic organization. In other words, Marx transforms Hegel's notion of alienated labor from an eternal anthropological into a transitory historical notion.

This reinterpretation carries a message of hope for mankind. Marx says that mankind is not condemned to live "by the sweat of his brow" under alienated conditions throughout his whole term on earth. He can become free, his labor can become free, he is capable of self-emancipation, though only under specific historical conditions. Later I will define what specific social and economic conditions are required for the disappearance of alienated labor.

Let us now pass from the first systematic exposition of his theory of alienation in the *Economic and Philosophic Manuscripts of 1844* to his main work, *Capital,* which was published over twenty years later. It is true that the word alienation hardly appears there.

A new profession has sprung up in the last thirty years called "Marxology." Its practitioners read through the works of Marx and put on small index cards all the words he uses in his books and then try to draw some conclusions about his thought from their philological statistics. Some people have even used computers in this type of formal analysis. These "Marx-philologists" have so far discovered six places in *Capital* where the word "alienation" is used either as a noun or as a verb. I certainly will not dispute that colossal discovery though somebody may find a seventh spot or there could be some dispute about the sixth one.

On the basis of such an analysis of *Capital,* done in a purely verbal and superficial way, it could be concluded that the mature Marx did not have a real theory of alienation. Marx would then have discarded it after his youth, after his immature development, especially when, around 1856/57, he became thoroughly convinced of the correctness of the labor theory of value and perfected that labor theory of value himself.

When the *Economic and Philosophic Manuscripts of 1844* were published for the first time in 1932, a big controversy arose around these issues. At least three trends can be distinguished in the debate. I will not cite the names of all the authors who have participated in it since more than a hundred people have written on the subject and the controversy is far from having ended. Some said there is a contradiction between the youthful and the mature works and Marx abandoned his original theories when his own views were fully developed.

Others said the opposite. The real Marx is to be found in the youthful works and he later degenerated by restricting the scope of his understanding to purely economic problems. He thus fell victim to the deviation of economism.

Still other people tried to deny that Marx's ideas underwent any significant or substantial evolution whatsoever. Among these are the American Erich Fromm, the French Marxist scholar Maximilien Rubel, and two French Catholic priests, Fathers Bigo and Colvez. They maintain that the same ideas are contained in his early as in his later works.

I think all three of these opinions are wrong. There was an important evolution, not an identical repetition, in Marx's thought from decade to decade. Any person who thinks, and continues to think and live, will not say exactly the same thing when he is sixty as when he was twenty-five. Even if it is conceded that the basic concepts remain the same, there is obviously some progress, some change. In this concrete case the evolution is all the more striking, as I said before, because the Marx of 1844 had not yet accepted the labor theory of value, which is a cornerstone of the economic theory he developed ten or fifteen years later.

One of the pivotal questions in this continuing debate is whether the mature Marx held a theory of alienation or whether he altogether abandoned his original theory of alienation. This dispute, which can be resolved on a documentary basis, would not have gone on so long and inconclusively if it had not been for another unfortunate accident.

It happened that another major work of Marx, *Gründrisse der Kritik der Politischen Ökonomie* ("Fundamental Outlines of a Critique of Political Economy"), a thirteen-hundred-page work written in 1857/58, which is a kind of laboratory where all the major ideas of *Capital* were first elaborated and tested, was also not published until a century after it was written. Its first publication occurred in Russia at the beginning of World War II, but most of the copies were destroyed as a result of the war. I believe only two copies arrived in the United States and none was available in Western Europe. The Russians under Stalin were not eager to reproduce it a second time. Thus it was not until the 1950s, almost a century after it had originally been written, that the book was reprinted and became known to a certain number of experts in a few countries.

Sad to say, this major work of Marx has still to be translated into English, although one has been announced. It appeared in French only a short time ago. So some of the participants in this dispute did have the excuse that they did not know that key work. For anybody who reads it can at once see that a Marxist theory of alienation exists because in the *Gründrisse* the word, the concept, and the analysis appear dozens and dozens of times.

When then is this theory of alienation as it was developed by the mature Marx, not by the young Marx? And how can we relate it to what is set down in *Capital?* There is first a purely formal difficulty here because Marx uses three different terms in this connection and he uses them in an interchangeable manner. One is the concept of alienation; another is the concept of reification, a complicated word; and a third is the concept of commodity fetishism, which is still more complicated.

However, these three concepts are not so difficult to explain, and I will try to clarify their meaning for you.

Let us start this analysis with a definition of economic alienation. I must immediately state that in the comprehensive Marxist theory of alienation, economic alienation is only one part of a much more general phenomenon that covers practically all fields of human activity in class society. But it is the most decisive element. So let's start from economic alienation. We will approach it in successive stages. The first and most striking feature of economic alienation is the separation of men from free access to the means of production and means of subsistence. This is a rather recent development in human history. As late as the nineteenth century free access to the means of production in agriculture survived in some countries of the world, among others, in the United States and Canada. Until after the American Civil War it was not impossible for masses of people to find some unpreempted spot of land and to establish themselves on that acreage as free farmers, as homesteaders. In Europe that possibility had ceased to exist for two hundred years, and in some countries there even three or four hundred years earlier.

That historical factor is the starting point for any theory of alienation because the institution of wage labor in which men are forced to sell their labor power to another person, to their employer, can come into existence on a large scale only when and where free access to the means of production and subsistence is denied to an important part of society. Thus the first precondition for the alienation of labor occurs when labor becomes separated from the basic means of production and subsistence.

I said this is a relatively new phenomenon. A second example may illuminate this more sharply. The classical historical criticism made by liberal thought in the nine-teenth century about the society of the Middle Ages, feudal society, was the lack of freedom of the cultivators of the soil. I won't take exception to that criticism, which I think was correct. The direct producers in that society, the peasants and serfs, were not free people. They could not move about freely; they were tied to the land.

But what the bourgeois liberal critics of feudal society forgot was that tying men to the land was a two-sided phenomenon. If man was tied to the land, the land was also tied to man. And because the land was tied to man, there wasn't any important part of the people living within feudal relations who could be forced to become wage laborers and sell their labor power to owners of capital. They had access to the land, they could produce their own means of subsistence and keep part of it for themselves. Only people outside organized feudal society, in reality outlaws, because that is what they were orig-inally, could become the starting point for new social classes—wage laborers on the one hand, merchants on the other.

The second stage in the alienation of labor came about when part of society was driven off the land, no longer had access to the means of production and means of sub-sistence, and, in order to survive, was forced to sell its labor power on the market. That is the main character-istic of alienated labor. In the economic field it is the institution of wage labor, the economic obligation of people who cannot otherwise survive to sell the only com-modity they possess, their labor power, on the labor market.

What does it mean to sell your labor power to a boss? In Marx's analysis, both in his youthful and his mature work, behind this purely formal and legal contractual relation—you sell your labor power, part of your time, to another for money to live on—is in reality something of deepgoing consequence for all human existence and particularly for the life of the wage laborer. It first of all implies that you lose control over a large part of your waking hours. All the time that you have sold to the employer belongs to him, not to you. You are not free to do what you want at work. It is the employer who dictates what you will and will not do during this whole time. He will dictate what you produce, how you produce it, where you produce it. He will be master over your activity.

And the more the productivity of labor increases and the shorter the workweek becomes, the stricter will be the control of the employer over every hour of your time as a wage laborer. In time and motion studies—the ultimate and most perfected form of this control—the boss even tries to control every second, *literally* every second, of the time that you spend in his employ.

Alienation thereupon acquires a third form. When a wage earner has sold his labor power for a certain part of his life to his employer, the products of his labor are not his own. The products of his labor become the property of the employer.

The fact that the modern wage earner owns none of the products of his own labor, obvious as it may appear to people who are accustomed to bourgeois society, is not at all so self-evident from the viewpoint of human history as a whole. It was not like that for thousands upon thousands of years of human existence. Both the medieval handicraftsman and the handicraftsman of antiquity were the proprietors of their own products. The peasant, and even the serf of the Middle Ages, remained in possession of at least fifty percent, sometimes sixty and seventy percent, of the output of their own labor.

Under capitalism not only does the wage earner lose possession of the product of his labor, but these products can function in a hostile and injurious manner against him. This happened with the machine. This remarkable product of human ingenuity becomes a source of tyranny against the worker when the worker serves as an append-age of the machine and is forced to adapt the cadence of his life and work to the operation of the machine. This can become a serious source of alienation in shift work when part of the working class has to work during the night or at odd hours, in conflict with the normal rhythm of human life between day and night. Such an abnormal schedule causes all sorts of psychological and nervous disorders.

Other aspects of the oppressive nature that the prod-ucts of labor can acquire once society is divided into hostile classes of capitalists and wage workers are the crises of overproduction, depressions or, as it is nowa-days more prudently put, recessions. Then people con-sume less because they produce too much. And they con-sume less, not because their labor is inadequately pro-ductive, but because their labor is too productive.

We come now to a final form of alienated labor in the economic field, which derives from the conclusions of the points I have noted. The alienation of the worker and his labor means that something basic has changed in the life of the worker. What is it? Normally everybody has some creative capacity, certain talents lodged in him, untapped potentialities for human development that should be expressed in his labor activity.

However, once the institution of wage labor is preva-lent, these possibilities become nullified. Work is no longer a means of self-expression for anybody who sells his labor time. Work is just a means to attain a goal. And that goal is to get money, some income to be able to buy the consumer goods necessary to satisfy your needs.

In this way a basic aspect of man's nature, his capacity

to perform creative work, becomes thwarted and distorted. Work becomes something that is not creative and productive for human beings but something that is harmful and destructive. Catholic priests and Protestant pastors who have worked in factories in Western Europe, the so-called worker-priests, who have written books about their experiences, have arrived at conclusions on this point that are absolutely identical with those of Marxism. They declare that a wage earner considers the hours passed in factories or in offices as time lost from his life. He must spend time there in order to get freedom and capacity for human development outside the sphere of production and of work.

Ironically, this hope for fulfillment during leisure time turns out to be an illusion. Many humanitarian and philanthropic reformers of liberal or social-democratic persuasion in the nineteenth and the beginning of the twentieth centuries thought that men could become liberated when their leisure time would increase. They did not understand that the nature of leisure was likewise determined by the nature of wage labor and by the conditions of a society based on commodity production and wage labor.

Once socially necessary labor time became shorter and leisure time greater, a commercialization of leisure took place. The capitalist society of commodity production, the so-called consumer society did its utmost to integrate leisure time into the totality of economic phenomena at the basis of commodity production, exploitation, and accumulation.

At this point the notion of alienation is extended from a purely economic to a broader social phenomenon. The first bridge to this wider application is the concept of alienation of the consumer. Thus far we have spoken only about the consequences of alienated labor. But one of the cardinal characteristics of capitalist society, as Marx understood as early as 1844, is its built-in contradiction regarding human needs. On the one hand, each capitalist entrepreneur tries to limit the human needs of his own wage earners as much as possible by paying as low wages as possible. Otherwise he would not make enough profit to accumulate.

On the other hand, each capitalist sees in the work force of all the other capitalists not wage earners but potential consumers. He would therefore like to expand the capacity of consumption of these other wage earners to the limit or otherwise he cannot increase production and sell what his own workers produce. Thus capitalism has a tendency constantly to extend the needs of people.

Up to a certain point this expansion can cover genuine human needs, such as the elementary requirements of feeding, housing, and clothing everybody in more or less decent circumstances. Very quickly, however, capitalism, in its efforts to commercialize everything and sell as many gadgets as possible, goes beyond any rational human needs and starts to spur and stimulate artificial needs in a systematic, large-scale manner. Some of these are absurd and grotesque. Let me give one example. An American author, Jessica Mitford, has written an amusing book called the *American Way of Death*. It describes the practices of morticians who seek to induce people to buy more expensive coffins so that the beloved dead can rest not only peacefully, but lightly, on foam mattresses. The sales pitchmen say this satisfies, not the corpse, but the feelings of the consumer.

Is it necessary to observe that no real need is involved in this grotesque attempt of the burial business to make money? It is scandalous to feed in this mercenary manner upon the feelings of grief of people who have lost members of their family.

Such alienation is no longer purely economic but has become social and psychological in nature. For what is the motivation of a system for constantly extending needs beyond the limits of what is rational? It is to create, purposely and deliberately, permanent and meretricious dissatisfactions in human beings. Capitalism would cease to exist if people were fully and healthily satisfied. The system must provoke continued artificial dissatisfaction in human beings because without that dissatisfaction the sales of new gadgets, which are more and more divorced from genuine human needs, cannot be increased.

A society that is turned toward creating systematic frustration of this kind generates the bad results recorded in the crime pages of the daily newspapers. A society that breeds worthless dissatisfaction will also breed all kinds of antisocial attempts to overcome this dissatisfaction.

Beyond this alienation of human beings as consumers, there are two very important aspects of alienation. One is the alienation of human activity in general. The other is the alienation of human beings in one of their most fundamental features, the capacity to communicate.

What is meant by the extension of the concept of alienation to human activity in general? We live in a society based on commodity production and a social division of labor pushed to the limits of overspecialization. As a result, people in a particular job or doing a certain type of activity for a living will incline to have an extremely narrow horizon. They will be prisoners of their trade, seeing only the problems and preoccupations of their specialty. They will also tend to have a restricted social and political awareness because of this limitation.

Along with this shut-in horizon will go something that

is much worse, the tendency to transform relations between human beings into relations between things. This
is that famous tendency toward "reification," the transformation of social relations into things, into objects, of
which Marx speaks in *Capital*.

This way of looking at phenomena is an extension of
this theory of alienation. Here is an example of this
transformation that I witnessed the other day in this
country. The waiters and waitresses in restaurants are
poor working people who are the victims and not the
authors of this process of reification. They are even unaware of the nature of their involvement in this phenomenon. While they are under heavy pressure to serve
the maximum number of customers on the job imposed
upon them by the system and its owners, they look upon
the customers solely under the form of the orders they
put in. I heard one waitress address herself to a person
and say, "Ah, you are the corned beef and cabbage."
You are not Mr. or Mrs. Brown, not a person of a certain age and with a certain address. You are "corned beef
and cabbage" because the waitress has on her mind the
orders taken under stress from so many people.

This habit of reification is not the fault of the inhu-
manity or insensitivity of the workers. It results from a
certain type of human relation rooted in commodity
production and its extreme division of labor where people engaged in one trade tend to see their fellows only as
customers or through the lenses of whatever economic
relations they have with them.

This outlook finds expression in everyday language. I
have been told that in the city of Osaka, the main commercial and industrial capital of Japan, the common
mode of addressing people when you meet is not "How
do you do?" but "How is business?" or "Are you making
money?" This signifies that bourgeois economic relations

have so completely pervaded ordinary human relations as to dehumanize them to an appreciable extent.

I come now to the ultimate and most tragic form of alienation, which is alienation of the capacity to communicate. The capacity to communicate has become the most fundamental attribute of man, of his quality as a human being. Without communication, there can be no organized society because without communication, there is no language, and without language, there is no intelligence. Capitalist society, class society, commodity-producing society tends to thwart, divert, and partially destroy this basic human capacity.

Let me give three examples of this process at three different levels, starting with a most commonplace case. How do men learn to communicate? While they are infants they go through what psychologists call a process of socialization and learn to speak. For a long time one of the main methods of socializing young children has been through playing with dolls. When a child plays with dolls, he duplicates himself, projects himself outside his own individuality, and carries on a dialogue with that other self. He speaks two languages, his own language and the language of the doll, thereby bringing into play an artificial process of communication, which, through its spontaneous nature, facilitates the development of language and intelligence.

Recently, industry started to produce dolls that speak. This is supposed to be a mark of progress. But once the doll speaks, the dialogue is limited. The child no longer speaks in two languages, or with the same spontaneity. Part of its speech is induced, and induced by some capitalist corporation.

That corporation may have hired the biggest educators and psychologists who make the doll speak more perfectly than any of the babble that could come out of the child's mind itself—although I have some doubts on that subject. Nevertheless, the spontaneous nature of the dialogue is partially thwarted, suppressed, or detoured. There is less development of dialogue, of capacity for communication, and therefore a lesser formation of intelligence than in more backward times when dolls did not speak and children had to give them a language of their own.

A second example is taken from a more sophisticated level. Any class society which is divided by social-material interests and in which class struggle goes on suppresses to a certain extent the capacity for communication between people standing on different sides of the barricades. This is not a matter of lack of intelligence, of understanding or honesty, from any individual point of view. This is simply the effect of the inhibitive pressures that substantial divisive material interests exercise on any group of individuals.

Anybody who has ever been present at wage bargaining where there is severe tension between workers' and employers' representatives—I'm talking about real wage bargaining, not sham wage bargaining—will understand what I am referring to. The employers' side simply cannot sympathize with or understand what the workers are talking about even if they have the utmost goodwill and liberal opinions, because their material-social interests prevent them from understanding what the other side is most concerned with.

There was a very striking example of this inhibition on another level (because workers and not employers were involved) in the tragic strike of the United Federation of Teachers in New York in 1968 against the decentralization of control over the school system. People of bad will, fools, or stupid people were not so much involved. Indeed, most of them would have been called liberal or even left some time ago. But through very strong pressures of social interest and social milieu, they were simply incapable of understanding what the other side, the Black and Puerto Rican masses who wanted community control over the education of their children, was talking about.

Thus the Marxist notion of alienation extends far beyond the oppressed classes of society, properly speaking. The oppressors are also alienated from part of their human capacity through their inability to communicate on a human basis with the majority of society. And this divorcement is inevitable as long as class society and its deep differentiations exist.

Another terrible expression of this alienation on the individual scale is the tremendous loneliness that a society based on commodity production and division of labor inevitably induces in many human beings. Ours is a society based on the principle: every man for himself. Individualism pushed to the extreme also means loneliness pushed to the extreme.

It is simply not true, as certain existentialist philosophers contend, that man has always been an essentially lonely human being. There have been forms of integrated collective life in primitive society where the very notion of loneliness could not arise. It arises out of commodity production and division of labor only at a certain stage of human development in bourgeois society. And then unfortunately it acquires a tremendous extension that can go beyond the limits of mental health.

Psychologists have gone around with tape recorders and listened to certain types of dialogues between people in shops or on the street. When they play these dialogues afterward they discover that there has been no exchange whatsoever. The two people have talked along parallel lines without once meeting with each other. Each talks because he welcomes the occasion to unburden himself, to get out of his loneliness, but he is incapable of listening to what the other person is saying.

The only meeting place is at the end of the dialogue when they say good-bye. Even that farewell is saddening because they want to save the possibility of unburdening themselves of their loneliness the next time they meet. They carry on what the French call *dialogue de sourds,* dialogues between deaf people, that is, dialogues between people who are incapable of understanding or listening to other people.

This is of course an extreme and marginal illustration. Happily, the majority of members of our society are not yet in that situation or otherwise we would be on the brink of a complete breakdown of social relations. Nonetheless, capitalism tends to extend the zone of this extreme loneliness with all its terrible implications.

This looks like a very dim picture, and the dim picture undoubtedly corresponds to the dim reality of our times. If the curve of mental sickness has climbed parallel with the curve of material wealth and income in most of the advanced countries of the West, this dismal picture has not been invented by Marxist critics but corresponds to very deep-rooted aspects of the social and economic reality in which we live.

But, as I said before, this grim situation is not at all without hope. Our optimism comes from the fact that, after all this analysis of the roots of the alienation of labor and the specific expressions of the alienation of man in bourgeois society is completed, there emerges the inescapable conclusion that a society can be envisaged in which there will be no more alienation of labor and alienation of human beings. This is a historically produced and man-made evil, not an evil rooted in nature or human nature. Like everything else that has been made by man, it can also be unmade by man. This condition is a product of history and it can be destroyed by history or at least gradually overcome by further progress.

Thus the Marxist theory of alienation implies and contains a theory of disalienation through the creation of conditions for the gradual disappearance and eventual abolition of alienation. I stress "gradual disappearance" because such a process or institution can no more be abolished by fiat or a stroke of the pen than commodity production, the state, or the division of society into classes can be eliminated by a government decree or proclamation.

Marxists understand that the social and economic preconditions for a gradual disappearance of alienation can be brought about only in a classless society ushered in by a world socialist revolution. And when I say a classless socialist society, I obviously do not mean the societies that exist in the Soviet Union, Eastern Europe, or China. In the best cases these are transitional societies somewhere halfway between capitalism and socialism. Though private property has been abolished, they have not yet abolished the division of society into classes, they still have different social classes and different social layers, division of labor and commodity production. As a consequence of these conditions, they still have alienated labor and alienated men.

The prerequisites for the disappearance of human alienation, of alienated labor and the alienated activities of human beings, can only be created precisely through the continuation of those processes I have just named: the withering away of commodity production, the disappearance of economic scarcity, the withering away of social division of labor through the disappearance of private ownership of the means of production, and the elimination of the difference between manual and intellectual labor, between producers and administrators. All of this would bring about the slow transformation of the very nature of labor from a coercive necessity in order to get money, income, and means of consumption into a voluntary occupation that people want to do because it covers their own internal needs and expresses their talents. This transformation of labor into all-sided creative human activity is the ultimate goal of socialism. Only when that goal is attained will alienated labor and all its pernicious consequences cease to exist.

THE HAPPY HABITAT *

Albert Eide Parr

. . . .

Aesthetics, as Albert Eide Parr points out, is not limited to phenomena labeled art. All our man-made surroundings are fair game for aesthetic speculation—whether beautiful or not is quite irrelevant. Parr defines aesthetics as "the science of our psychological responses to our sensory perceptions" and it follows that the environment "must offer a sufficiently rich, fine-grained, enduring, and varied diversity of forms and colors to offer satisfactory stimulus fields for all its inhabitants."

In fact, this article is a plea for comprehensive appreciation of the urban environment. Parr believes in the variety, density, and worth of urban surroundings and says "the urban setting could be made as attractive as any human habitat ever was. . . ." He suggests different ways of looking and learning that are conditioned from the position, movement, and surroundings of the observer. In order to satisfy man's essential instincts toward curiosity (and learning), we need "the

* Reprinted from *The Journal of Aesthetic Education*, Vol. 6, No. 3 (July, 1972).

enchantment of spaces charmingly defined on the human scale," rather than "beautiful monoliths to be seen like distant pyramids in the desert. . . ."

In architecture and urban design, all too often the role of people as aesthetic elements is denied. Parr, citing examples as diverse as Rome's "Spanish Stairs" to the Pan American building in New York, observes that "The successful artistic creation of human habitats calls for a much more conscious and explicit inclusion of the inhabitants, both on the artist's palette and on his canvas." What he means is that good design, in every area, depends not upon theory and formal principles but rather upon authentic realization of the opportunities for human enjoyment. Therein lies the challenge for art and artist. "Art can rise to greater heights in the service of mankind than in the service of the machine and the artistic ego."

That it is the legitimate concern of the artist-educator to instruct citizens on how to enjoy urban crowding, will come as a surprise to some. Yet urban amenities are what they are because of density of population. A plaza in front of every skyscraper may not be such a good idea after all.

Albert Eide Parr is Director Emeritus of the American Museum of Natural History. This article was presented as a talk to a conference on "The Aesthetic Environment" sponsored by the Department of Philosophy at Temple University, under a grant from the National

Endowment for the Humanities, November 13/14, 1970.

. . . .

Perhaps the greatest difficulty of our subject lies in the definition of its terms. Our environment is the entire universe. When we speak of the aesthetic environment we presumably limit our discussion to the surroundings perceived through our senses. We exclude the oil deposits deep in the earth that supply us with heat and energy, but concern ourselves about the oil slick destroying the attractions of the Santa Barbara harbor and coastline. We also confine ourselves to a consideration of the environment as we perceive it, not as it actually is. We worship the sun with total disregard for what its forces would do to us if the sun itself should cross our path. But with today's means of visual communication the restriction of our subject matter to the perceived images of our surroundings rather than to their remote or concealed realities is not so helpful as it might have been. My visits to Italy have never taken me south of Rome, but films and pictures have given me a very vivid portrait of the charms of Naples. I should feel it as a loss to my aesthetic environment if Naples, though never seen by me, should go the way of Pompeii. I saw Singapore and Nagasaki more than fifty years ago. For one reason or another, many of the features that enchanted me on my youthful visits to both places have since vanished, and my own little world has been bereaved thereby.

To render our subject manageable let us therefore eliminate both the images of memory and those of vicarious experience, except to the extent that they may influence our responses to the sensory aspects of our immediate surroundings. This is a very important exception, but there is no way to avoid it, and even such a conditional exclusion of past and secondary exposures to milieu is of considerable help in defining the topic of our discussion, which has now been reduced to the aesthetics of the directly perceived fields of our daily habitat. But we still have the concept of aesthetics to contend with.

"Aesthetics" is a word of many definitions, ranging from the philosophy and principles of the fine arts to the broad science of sensuous knowledge. The aesthetics of our habitat can obviously not be circumscribed by the fine-arts aspects of our surroundings, architectural or otherwise. The connotations extend even beyond the entire compass of human artifacts, for example, to the moon and the mountaintops as they enter the view through our picture window. But any definition of aesthetics we may use will, sooner or later, get us involved with the notion of beauty, which is an even more poorly defined abstraction than those we have attempted to deal with so far, although such a thing would scarcely seem possible.

Actually "beauty" is a collective term for many different categories of particulars and effects. To untangle the diversity and interrelations of the varied and often conflicting manifestations grouped under the heading of beauty would require much more time and space than the subject warrants in this context. But since we are directing ourselves to the problems of man's creation of his own surroundings we may need to remind ourselves that no man's vision of beauty can ever be made an all-pervading feature of the landscape without being destroyed thereby, because the commonplace is never beautiful. There is no definition of beauty that can serve as a usable criterion for the overall strategic goals of our efforts, although the concept is very helpful at tactical levels. Our ultimate aim must be the creation of surroundings in which a sense of joy and well-being is likely to flourish. Environmental design alone, of course, cannot guarantee such a result, any more than a well-tended field can give absolute assurance of a fine crop. But without a fertile soil we can be certain of a poor harvest. We must learn how to cultivate the aesthetic environment to produce a greater and better yield of happy habitats than mankind now enjoys, and this will be the essence of my purpose.

Happiness is a state of mind that is hard to appraise, and it is even more difficult to apportion credit for our bliss among the many sources of its origins. Fortunately there are symptoms that are more easily assessed than are the qualities of the basic condition itself. The persons, things, and circumstances that provide, abet, and attend our joys become objects of our love. In individual cases the situation may be confused by the transfer of feelings from primary causes to associated scenes and elements. Yet when love for locale is common and strong among the inhabitants and quickly smites the visitors, we know that we are in an environment offering fertile ground for the seeds of happiness.

There is not, and can never be, a final design answer to the quest for a happy habitat. The problem is not static but dynamic. A certain amount of change and novelty is an essential prerequisite for the enjoyment of the days and years of our lives. The task of environmental design is not to provide a terminal retirement home for our civilization, but to guide the evolution of our surroundings in such a manner that we may find delight and assurance both in the process and in the stages it takes us through.

The dangers of the static view of the issues of milieu are often further compounded by the simplistic notion that the problems of design are features of a strictly binary situation between fits and misfits. But the happiness we should strive for is not just the absence of discontent. One misfit among many may turn into an asset when other incompatibilities disappear A world in which all irritants and imperfections had been removed by a purely negative process of elimination or neutralization might make it difficult to formulate any specific complaint, but it would be an exceedingly dull world to live in. What we need is an optimization of incongruities to maintain our mental and emotional tone, without overstrain, as physical challenges maintain the tone of our muscles. This is one of the factors involved in Ivor de Wolfe's assertion [1] that good townscape often comes out of bad architecture whereas good architecture often makes bad townscape. Such thoughts and observations lead directly to an essential qualification of the symptomatic characteristic used in defining the ultimate aim of environmental design.

Lovable surroundings may be relaxing to the point of indolence. A stimulating milieu may be exhausting and painful to live with. Our concepts of beauty may apply to either, but neither one alone can give us the qualities of a happy habitat. We need a healthy mixture of both. As I have stated before,[2] I find the prospects of London and Paris both stimulating and lovable, although the features I would call beautiful are few and far between, and the districts most fondly and stirringly remembered may have none. The connotations of beauty fail to convey the true charisma of the man-made milieu. And if a city is stimulating and lovable, who should care whether the arbiters of style and taste can certify that it is also beautiful? But, in its restricted role, the concept of beauty is still a very convenient one to use in any discussion of art or nature, as long as the limitations upon its significance are clearly understood.

Although the aesthetics of the happy habitat involves much more than a simple concern about beauty, the sub-

[1] *The Italian Townscape* (New York: George Braziller, 1966).
[2] A. E. Parr, "The City as Habitat," *The Centennial Review*, Vol. 14, No. 2 (1970).

ject is not all-inclusive in its scope. It does not include the logistics of life support either for the individual or for the community, except as the operations may become part of our sensuous knowledge of our surroundings. Our senses are aware of most of our bodily needs, but unless their fulfillment offers sensory rewards beyond mere consciousness of physical gratification, it need, perhaps, not be regarded as an aesthetic experience. We might say that neither getting chilled outdoors nor coming inside to get warm is an aesthetic event per se. But, from such incidents we form associations that make us respond to buildings and landscapes as warm or cold, hostile or friendly. To escape from this endless chain of ambiguities I like to think of aesthetics as the science of our psychological responses to our sensory perceptions, rather than the broader science of sensuous knowledge in itself, or the narrower philosophy of artistic principles.

It is clear that every sense modality has its own aesthetic, and also that the simultaneous input through all of our senses provides a total experience that is more than the sum of its parts. But, in this context, visual images are our principal concern.

As has already been stated too often to require reiteration in detail, our minds have needs of sensory intake quite similar to our bodily appetites for food. For the young, for most people of any age, and for a pluralistic society that wishes to remain pluralistic, a most basic demand upon the environment is that it must offer a sufficiently rich, fine-grained, enduring, and varied diversity of forms and colors to offer satisfactory stimulus fields for all its inhabitants.

We need only remind ourselves of the need of young, developing minds for variety in their sensory intake. Without it they become dull.[3] We must also remember

[3] A. E. Parr, "City and Psyche," *The Yale Review,* Vol. 55, No. 1 (1965).

the small dimensions of the child's autonomous orbit, which means that we must make available within a block or two environmental stimulation equivalent to or exceeding what might be adequate for the entire crosstown journeys of the adults.

The crux of our problem is that our technology is changing, or causing us to alter, our habitat much faster than biological process will permit us to evolve new minds and bodies to fit the new circumstances. Even stud-farm breeding of people for human beehives would not enable us to catch up. We are therefore still saddled with needs that were assets or enjoyable appetites before, but have become temporary burdens to us now until we can find new ways of meeting old demands to increase our joy in living. Our problem becomes more understandable in a comparison between town and country, the present and the recent past.

On the nineteenth-century farm the small child had the freedom, within limits, of house, barn, and yard—a world filled and surrounded by a tremendous multitude of sights, sounds, smells, objects, and events in any comparison with the central plaza of a modern high-rise housing development or the best-equipped playpen or urban nursery school. The flight of young families to the suburbs is undoubtedly in a large measure a flight from the physical risks and uniformities of metropolis in an effort to restore to their youngest some of the pleasures of life in the country. Given what the cities have become today, one can hardly criticize this retreat from their precincts, but it is my firm conviction that the urban setting could be made as attractive as any human habitat ever was, even for the youngest, if those who design our surroundings would always face the problem in its totality, and not one aspect at a time. I know that there are some who valiantly seek the overall solution, and I believe the survival of our cities may, in the long run, depend upon their support and their success.

Curiosity is the appetite of the mind. It expresses itself as a craving for exploration and adventure, and in the most uninhibited fashion among the young. It is a universal characteristic of all higher forms of life, as any animal-lover knows.

As time passes our potential orbit increases, while the near at hand is gradually depleted of new discoveries and adventures. In the country the teen-ager could engage in progressively more wide-ranging daily activities —tending the animals in the fields, exploring the countryside, hunting, fishing, logging, and so on—with his elders, his peers, or alone. Half-acre lots in the suburbs offer no such opportunities for expanding horizons. Even in their present, deplorable condition the central cities offer greater inducements to inquisitive teen-age minds than they can find in satellite communities. And when adventure is denied by the environment it is quite likely to be sought in behavioral conflicts with the milieu.[4] Juvenile delinquency born of boredom is rife in the suburbs.

We have made this detour through exurbia primarily to show that there is no ideal and universal solution for the urban problem by retreat from metropolis, although such action may be the lesser evil for some and in some situations. But the greatest happiness for all is that which can only be found in a habitat that serves us equally well at all ages and in all circumstances. Only the city's pluralism of forms, people, and institutions offers any real hope of achieving such a condition, however bleak the prospects may look at the moment.

Ian Nairn [5] has said that "a walk in town can be as

[4] A. E. Parr, "The Five Ages of Urbanity," *Landscape*, Vol. 17, No. 3 (1968).

[5] *The American Landscape* (New York: Random House, 1965).

refreshing and exhilarating as a Scotch-on-the-rocks after a hot, tiring day." There are still cities or precincts that provide the refreshment Nairn speaks of, but their numbers have been declining while urban populations multiply, and the trip between work and home has become another dreary burden added to the chores of the day. In metropolis the amenities of the road are primarily, and almost exclusively, those you are able to enjoy on foot. In the suburbs, the view through the windshield may add a good bit to the satisfactions of everyday existence, but when you must try to maneuver your car on workaday errands through metropolitan precincts, you pick your route according to actual or anticipated traffic conditions in the streets and not according to the values of the vistas. Their efficiency as traffic sewers is virtually the only amenity of the thoroughfares that you are conscious of and able to give any great attention to. Even as passengers in private automobiles we tend to identify so much with the driver and his problems that we make little use of our freedom to take a broader view of our surroundings. Our foot presses against a pedal that is not there to help brake the car to a stop. Riding in a bus or streetcar our identification with the operator becomes more tenuous, if not absent altogether, and sightseeing is more relaxed and enjoyable. On such a ride we may also be able to notice a very significant difference between the way we observe our surroundings at a halt and when our conveyance is moving freely and rapidly through the cityscape. In the prospects seen from a moving vehicle, the viewer gets his satisfactions and his information principally from the more distant and larger features of which the street has little to offer within its restricted confines. The small and near at hand that is the main and most rewarding ingredient of the pedestrian stimulus field in the central city is of little value on wheels, except as clues for the operation of the vehicle. It is true, of course, that even in the confinement of city streets a limited spectrum of environmental gratifications may reach the awareness of the traveler by car. Our motion does not greatly affect the charms of the view from the bridge, or the magic of occasional broad panoramas seen from rare vantage points within the urban milieu. Nevertheless, it is scarcely a simplification to say that the amenities of the central city we are concerned with here are those we experience when moving about under our own power, alone.

The townscape derives its attractions and its flaws principally from two sources: the works of man and his presence on the scene. Sometimes the topography lends the urban designer a very helping hand. Between the view across the harbor of a seaport and the view across the street, one might then expect that there would be many vistas offering effective attractions for pedestrians, on intermediate scales. In the older cities of Western civilization this is often true. But in newer urban areas, spawned by the industrial revolution, it is rarely the case. It would appear that when the view is closed by man-made structures, either in the near or the middle distance, sustained attraction requires an enrichment of the scene at eye level, which is now generally considered to conflict with the solemn dignity of public plazas, cultural centers, and the like. Indeed it is a commandment of modern architectural faith that the simplicity of treatment so essential for good appearance where the higher levels recede from our close observation of detail must be extended consistently into the ground. We build beautiful monoliths to be seen like distant pyramids in the desert, whereas we need the enrichment of spaces charmingly defined on the human scale.

The human scale is actually not a scale, but a gradient. The dimensions of the precipitous El Capitan are quite as overwhelming as those of the Pan American building, if not more so, but they do not appear that way from most points of observation: there is always a graduated sequence of lesser forms—small flowers near the ground, shrubs, boulders, and majestic trees—leading your eye from the spot where you stand to the peak against the sky. When the gradient is eliminated or drastically abbreviated, oppressive effects result. Thinking back to Norway, where I grew up, I realize from memory that nature can be just as inhuman in its "scale" as anything made by men, when, for example, a precipice rises nakedly out of a fjord with no gradient to soften its impact.

But the human gradient need not extend through all dimensions of space and time; it can also be contained within the two dimensions of a plane. Without its magnificent exterior murals the library of Mexico's University City would seem a harshly inhuman block of concrete. The concept of a human gradient, to make outlandish dimensions in our surroundings more comfortable to live with, is not identical with the theory of scale as a necessary means of generating a sense of security by enabling the observer to take the measure of what he sees. The two ideas are not in conflict; rather, they supplement each other. Elements of scale allowing easy assessment of actual heights would scarcely relieve the vertiginous impact of a bold precipice, or a hundred-story skyscraper façade, on a spectator approaching its base. A human gradient in two or in three dimensions would loosen the hypnotic hold of mere size upon the mind and invite our attention to travel over the entire scene before us, to achieve a more balanced and less disturbing impression of the whole. At the other extreme, and in the middle range of magnitudes, a lack of clues to actual measurements may spoil the effectiveness of design and create dissatisfaction where pleasure was intended. Some familiar object or motif may have to be introduced into the perspectives in order to make the dimensions comprehensible and thereby enjoyable.

When I hear architectural protests against applied ornamentation, my thoughts always turn to the sister discipline of naval architecture. In boat design, functional effectiveness is so essential that a theory of functionalism could never be seriously debated. Perhaps for that very reason ship designers never seem to have developed any guilty consciences about adding features solely intended for mental and emotional effects, with no relationship to physical performance. From my own earliest years in Norway I can remember how the growing girth and numbers of smokestacks gave visual testimony of the increasing powers invisibly buried in the depth of the hull. As we know, the mental association of funnels with strength and seagoing capabilities became so firmly entrenched in the popular reaction to the image of a ship that false smokestacks, not performing their ostensible functions, were often added for the sole purpose of visibly proclaiming the very real powers hidden within.

In the planning of the human habitat the people themselves must be dealt with as components of the milieu, and not merely as respondents to its faults or virtues. It was in two museums that I first became fully aware of the role of my fellow citizens as aesthetic elements in the architecture of my surroundings. A temporary exposition hall had survived its original purpose and been converted to museum use. I first saw it when there were no visitors and found its cavernous gloom ugly and depressing. I returned on a Sunday when it had full attendance, with the bright colors of the women's summer dresses mingling with the more conservative tones of masculine attire and children swarming around. The overview from the balcony was now more enchanting than all the exhibits I had seen on my first visit. An art museum in another part of the country had devoted one of its halls to a glass-enclosed exhibit of mandarin costumes, which were shown on platforms raised to a little below shoulder height. There were few spectators the first time I entered the hall. Mental images of mandarins looked down upon us with great dignity from the thronelike elevation of their pedestals. Pleasingly proportioned entrance and exit archways lent a mild suggestion of nobility to the entire scene. I came back when the hall was full. The mandarins looked as if they had been hastily and precariously rescued from the crush of the mob. The archways, seen only from the shoulder level and up, looked squat and oppressive, more reminiscent of warehouses than of stately homes.

In these two examples I had seen completely opposite aesthetic effects produced by the presence of crowds in indoor spaces. Outdoors we have all experienced how dreary some of the most enchanting streets and plazas can look in their emptiness at the wrong hours of the day or night, but also how serene other vistas may become when there are few to share them with you.

In the renderings of their plans and prospectuses, architects and urban designers do, of course, usually show some human figures. But it is difficult to avoid the impression that the images of our species are used more for scale and decoration of the page than as representations of the intended aesthetics of reality. The successful artistic creation of human habitats calls for a much more conscious and explicit inclusion of the inhabitants, both on the artist's palette and on his canvas. Since I do not know of any clear discussion of the aesthetics of the human presence in the cityscape, I shall offer a few suggestions of what seems to me to illustrate a great range of aesthetic possibilities, hoping that enough of you will agree with me to prove that I am not merely expressing purely personal idiosyncracies.

To achieve their aesthetic completion, a stadium or an amphitheater must be full, while the Spanish Stairs must not, but neither should the Stairs be empty. It is my feeling that both Trafalgar Square and Piccadilly Circus look their best in their most crowded hours. The new City Hall in Boston seems to have the rare distinction of providing an equally superb aesthetic background for a few stragglers or a crowd in its plaza. I. M. Pei is the architect of two outstanding buildings that interest me very much because of their intermediate position in relation to the aesthetics of the human herd. Looking up at the Royal Bank of Canada from the plaza covering the Ville Marie in Montreal is like gazing in awe at the soaring rigging of a ship. But it takes a reasonable sense of solitude to appreciate the effect. A packed crowd would spoil it, as would passengers rail to rail on the deck at sea. The NCAR building at Boulder, Colorado, fits its environment so perfectly that it seems to have risen out of the ground. Some people around it give life to the scene, like deer on a mountainside, but a large crowd would seem as out of place as standing-room-only in the Garden of the Gods. And then, we have some much-admired pieces of architecture that contemptuously treat humanity, singly or in crowds, as unwelcome intruders among gargantuan funerary obelisks and mausoleums. The role of man as an aesthetic ingredient of his milieu may thus differ very widely according to circumstances, but it is a failure of urban design when the proper human attendance for the fulfillment of the design's aesthetic purpose does not materialize. To me the Civic Center Plaza in San Francisco is an example of such failure that might help us to avoid its repetition.

In the country, plant and animal life, wild and

domestic, introduces a third major element into the prospects of our habitat, perhaps fully as important in the vistas as either man or his works. This element has always been of less consequence in the townscape, and, with the virtual disappearance of the horse from city streets, it has been reduced to the role of an extra on the stage. But this raises the question of the aesthetic significance of the motor vehicles that are the successors to the horses in urban precincts.

As I surveyed my memories of places where human crowds might be missed, or found objectionable by their presence, I also thought about the automobiles. When I discovered that the upright London taxicabs and the double-decker buses were the only vehicles I could think of that I would really mourn for if they should disappear from my vision of the urban landscape, I became concerned about growing prematurely old at the early age of seventy. But when I thought some more about it, I found other, and more acceptable, reasons for my feelings.

The upright cabs and tall buses seem the last of the generation of vehicles consciously, or unconsciously, designed in the image of friendly human accommodations on wheels. The cars that came later have been shaped and sold as expressions of the individual's withdrawal and competitive belligerence on the road. The spirit of isolation and hostility permeates the advertising, and the automobiles seem reminiscent of sharks and barracudas gliding through the Garden of Eden of a tropical coral reef. If the auto makers had not catered to the worst in their customers, perhaps there might have been slightly less antipathy against the presence of their products in the cityscape. Today, of course, the question is academic because there are so many other reasons for the maximum possible exclusion of private automobiles from the urban milieu.

The classical constituents of the world we live in are

air, land, and water. As a basic necessity water is of prime importance everywhere, but it appears in the picture of our surroundings only in particular locations, which there is no time to consider here. The air, however, is omnipresent and cannot be left out of even the most general treatment of our subject.

Air means weather, and weather adds up to climate. In the days of architecture without architects man fitted his shelter to the climate he lived in. The New England farmhouses we admire so much, among the birches and pines of the north, were not built under the palms on West Indian beaches, although there is always Willemstad, pretending to be a town in Holland, to remind us that there is no rule without exceptions. In new construction, throughout large parts of the Western world, international building techniques and architectural concepts have almost completely erased the old regional differences related to natural raw materials and natural conditions, including climate. This has been a gain in some ways, but in other respects it has presented a loss, particularly in regard to psychological needs.

The primary purpose of any building is to provide shelter against the forces of the exterior surroundings. This has been true since the cavemen, and will be till the end of the world. If it were not, we could, and should, dispense with buildings altogether. But effective shelter is not only a question of physical defense against the inclemencies of the sun and the atmosphere, and other unwelcome intrusions into our lives; it is also a matter of psychological reassurance about being securely protected. We should again remind ourselves of the comforting superfluity of smokestacks on the transatlantic liners.

Before the fluorescent tubes were yet on the general market, I obtained some for a couple of museum halls. You may recall that the early tubes had a very cold, bluish-white light. We immediately began to get complaints from our visitors about being cold in these halls, although we could prove that the temperatures were just as high—in one case higher—as in the rest of the museum. There are forms and colors that make you feel warm and protected whatever the realities may be. There are others that make you feel cool and serene, and yet others that make you feel cold, exposed, and uncomfortable. I have heard secretaries in Hartford and in Winnipeg complain about getting the shivers during the winter in well-heated rooms behind glass walls. There is an office building in Milwaukee and two famous high-rise apartment houses in Chicago that make me hesitate to leave the warm embrace of neighboring streets when the thermometer registers fifteen below. In the design of our habitat we should pay as close attention to climate as we do in the planning of an airport, and we should use the aesthetics of our design to reinforce the physical provisions we must make.

Whether our urban designers like it or not, the members of our species will always have to go through childhood before growing up. In childhood they will be conditioned to many perceptual images that might not make such a strong and lasting impression if they were not experienced until the years of our maturity. Except when there is a compelling reason to do so, for the good of all, intelligent and well-meaning architects and urban designers should not force their fellowmen to go through the stresses and strains of reconditioning, again and again, wasting nervous energies that could be better used for the enjoyment of life and to give greater endurance under tensions that are really unavoidable. Great artists should use our early conditioning as part of the material with which they work to lead us toward an ever greater sense of being at home in the world, and I believe they did their best to do so until the twentieth century. This did not, and would not, mean an end to aesthetic progress and to the evolution of new artistic concepts. It simply means that art can rise to greater heights in the service of mankind than in the service of the machine and the artistic ego.

Only when the urban designers learn how to mix the proper blend of people, spaces, action, memories, climate, and architecture shall we achieve the happy habitat we are striving for.

Part Two

· · · · · · · · · · · · · · · · · · ·

EDUCATION
FOR
THE ARTIST

THE EDUCATION OF THE UN-ARTIST, PART I *

Allan Kaprow

. . . .

According to Kaprow, it is the everyday, or ". . . global environment . . ." as opposed to the specialized artistic environment that ". . . will engage us in an increasingly participational way." In this essay Kaprow completely rejects traditional artistic energies and establishments to the extent that ". . . the artist of the future must learn how to evade his profession."

Kaprow's criticisms take into consideration the problem of art, which claims to edify but in fact the far greater and more effective value changes are brought about ". . . by political, military, economic, technological, educational, and advertising pressures." He adds: "The arts . . . have been poor lessons, except possibly to artists and their tiny publics." Kaprow suggests that to see the situation ". . . as low comedy is a way out of the bind," and proposes that artists ". . . avoid all aesthetic roles, give up all references to being artists of any kind whatever."

* Reprinted from *Art News*, Vol. 69, No. 10 (February, 1971).

Artists on both sides of the Atlantic have already engaged in actions similar to those proposed by Kaprow. And art educators—abandoning formalized art education for a broader "life education"—have carried his suggestions to imaginative and daring lengths, as indicated by other contributors to this book.

Kaprow recognizes the ". . . historical thrust of the modern arts toward specialism . . ." yet feels that "intermedia" activity is more appropriate to contemporary realities. "It makes no difference whether this is called activism, criticism, pranksterism, self-advertisement, or art. Intermedia implies fluidity and simultaneity of roles." In this vein the author echoes Buckminster Fuller's belief, "With every one keeping eyes on his own work, all the looking is quite shortsighted in both time and geography. It's left to the military to keep eyes on the world . . ." *

The author indicates that for the future "Agencies for the spread of information by way of the mass media, and for the instigation of social activities, will become the new channels of insight and communication . . ." and he predicts that as far as academic art departments are concerned, ". . . the conventions of painting, music, architecture, dance, poetry, theatre, and so on, may survive in a marginal capacity as academic researches . . ."

The sweeping pronouncements, concerning the viability of art and of education for art, contained in this article add up to a

---

* Buckminster Fuller, *et al.*, *Approaching the Benign Environment* (New York: Collier Books, 1971) , p. 59.

> *major challenge as well as a demand for*
> *change. The author is widely recognized as a*
> *leading theorist in art, and is regarded as hav-*
> *ing originated the art form of mixed media,*
> *known as the Happening. He teaches at the*
> *California Institute of the Arts.*

. . . .

Sophistication of consciousness in the arts today (1969) is so great that it is hard not to assert as matters of fact:

that the LM mooncraft is patently superior to all contemporary sculptural efforts;

that the broadcast verbal exchange between Houston's Manned Spacecraft Center and the Apollo 11 astronauts was better than contemporary poetry;

that, with its sound distortions, beeps, static, and communication breaks, such exchanges also surpassed the electronic music of the concert halls;

that certain remote-control videotapes of the lives of ghetto families, recorded (with their permission) by anthropologists, are more fascinating than the celebrated slice-of-life underground films;

that not a few of those brightly lit, plastic and stainless-steel gas stations of, say, Las Vegas are the most extraordinary architecture to date;

that the random, trancelike movements of shoppers in a supermarket are richer than anything done in the modern dance;

that the lint under beds and the debris of industrial dumps are more engaging than the recent rash of exhibitions of scattered waste matter;

that the vapor trails left by rocket tests—motionless, rainbow-colored, sky-filling scribbles—are unequaled by artists exploring gaseous mediums;

that the Southeast Asian theatre of war in Vietnam, or the trial of the "Chicago Eight," while indefensible, is better theatre than any play;

that . . . etc., etc., . . . non-art is more art than Art-art.

MEMBERS OF THE CLUB (PASSWORDS IN AND OUT)

Non-art is obviously whatever has not yet been accepted as art, but has caught an artist's attention with that possibility in mind. For those concerned, non-art (password one) exists only fleetingly if at all, like some subatomic particle, or perhaps only as a postulate. Indeed, the moment any such example is offered publicly, it automatically becomes a type of art. Let's say I am impressed by the mechanical clothes conveyors commonly used in dry-cleaning shops. Flash! While they continue to perform their normal work of roller-coastering me my suit in twenty seconds flat, they double as Kinetic Environments. Simply because I had the thought and have written it here. By the same process all the examples listed in the paragraphs above are conscripts of art. Art is very easy nowadays.

Because art is so easy, there is a growing number of artists who are interested in this paradox and wish to prolong its resolution, if only for a week or two, for the life of non-art is precisely its fluid identity. Art's former "difficulty" in the actual making stages may be transposed in this case to an arena of collective uncertainty over just what to call the critter: sociology, hoax, therapy? A Cubist portrait in 1910, before it was labeled a mental aberration, was self-evidently a *painting*. Blowing up successively closer views of an aerial map (a fairly typical example of 1960s "site art") might more obviously suggest an aerial bombing plan.

Non-art's advocates, according to this description, are those who consistently, or at one time or other, have chosen to operate outside the pale of art establishments, that is, in their heads, or in the daily or natural domain. At all times, however, they have informed the art establishments of their activities, to set into motion the uncertainties without which their acts would have no meaning. The art-not-art dialectic is essential—one of the nice ironies I shall return to several times hereafter.

Among this group, some of whom do not know each other, or, if they do, do not like each other, are "concept" makers such as George Brecht, Ben Vautier, and Joseph Kosuth, "found sound" guides such as Max Neuhaus, "earthworkers" such as Dennis Oppenheim and Michael Heizer, some of the 1950s Environment builders, and such Happeners as Milan Kňižák, Marta Minujín, Kazuo Shiraga, Wolf Vostell and myself.

But sooner or later most of them and their colleagues throughout the world have seen their work absorbed into the cultural institutions against which they initially measured their liberation. Some have wished it this way; it was, to use Paul Brach's expression, like paying their dues to join the union. Others have shrugged it off, continuing the game in new ways. But all have found that password one won't work.

Non-art often is confused with the older mode of "anti-art" (password two), which in Dadatime and even earlier was non-art aggressively (and wittily) intruded into the arts world to jar conventional values and provoke positive aesthetic and/or ethical responses. Alfred Jarry's *Ubu Roi* (1896), Erik Satie's and Darius Milhaud's *Furniture Music* (1920), and Marcel Duchamp's *Fountain* (1917) are familiar examples. The late Sam Goodman's New York exhibition some years ago of varieties of sculpted dung piles was still another. Non-art has no such intent; and intent is part of both function and feeling in any situation that deliberately blurs its operational context.

Apart from the question of whether or not the historical arts have ever demonstrably caused anybody to become "better," or "worse," for that matter, and granting that, even so, all art has presumed to edify in *some* way (perhaps only to prove that nothing can be proven), such avowedly moralistic programs appear naïve today in the light of the far greater and more effective value changes brought about by political, military, economic, technological, educational, and advertising pressures. The arts, at least up to the present, have been poor lessons, except possibly to artists and their tiny publics. Only these vested interests have ever made any high claims for the arts. The rest of the world couldn't care less. Anti-art, non-art, or other such cultural designations, share, after all, the word "art" or its implicit presence, and so point to a family argument at best, if they do not reduce utterly to tempests in teapots. And that is true for the bulk of this discussion.

When Steve Reich suspends a number of microphones above corresponding loudspeakers, sets them swinging like pendulums, and amplifies their sound pickup so that feedback noise is produced—that's art.

When Andy Warhol publishes the unedited transcript of twenty-four hours of taped conversation—that's art.

When Walter De Maria fills a room full of dirt—that's art.

We know they are art, obviously, because a concert announcement, a title on a book jacket, and an art gallery say so.

If non-art is almost impossible, anti-art is virtually inconceivable. Among the knowledgeable (and practically every graduate student should qualify), all gestures, thoughts, and deeds may become art at the whim of the arts world. Even murder could be an admissible artistic proposition although rejected in practice. Anti-art in 1969 is embraced in *every case* as pro-art, and therefore, from the standpoint of one of its chief functions, it is nullified. You cannot be against art when art invites its own "destruction" as a Punch-and-Judy act among the repertory of poses art may take. And so in losing the last shred of pretense to moral leadership through moral confrontation, anti-art, like all other art philosophies, simply is obliged to answer to ordinary human conduct; and also, sadly enough, answer to the refined life-style dictated by the cultivated and rich who accept it with open arms.

When Richard Artschwager discreetly pastes little black oblongs on parts of buildings across California, has a few photos to show and stories to tell—that's art.

When George Brecht prints on small cards sent to friends the words "DIRECTION. Over There"—that's art.

When Ben Vautier signs his name (or God's) to any airport—that's art.

These acts are obviously art because they are made by persons associated with the arts.

It's to be expected that in spite of the paradoxical awareness referred to at the beginning of this article, Art-art (password three) is the condition, both in the mind and literally, in which every novelty comes to rest. Art-art takes art *seriously*. It presumes, however covertly, to a certain spiritual rarity, a superior office. It has faith. It is recognizable by its initiates. It innovates, of course, but largely in terms of a tradition of professionalistic moves and references: art begets art. Most of all, Art-art maintains for its exclusive use certain sacred settings and formats handed down by this tradition: exhibitions, books, recordings, concerts, arenas, shrines, civic monuments, stages, film screenings, and the "culture" columns of the mass media. These grant accreditation the way universities grant degrees.

So long as Art-art holds on to these contexts, it can and often does costume itself in nostalgic echoes of anti-art, a reference that critics correctly observed in Robert Rauschenberg's earlier shows. It is self-evident in later Pop painting and writing, which make deliberate use of common clichés in content and method. Art-art can also assert the features, though not the milieu, of non-art, as in much of the music of John Cage. In fact, Art-art in the guise of non-art quickly became high style during the 1968/69 season at the Castelli Gallery warehouse shows of informal dispersions of felt, metal, rope, and other raw matter. Shortly afterward, this quasi-non-art received its virtual apotheosis at the Whitney Museum's presentation of similar stuff, called "Anti-Illusion: Procedures/ Materials" (1969). There, contained in the title, a hint of anti-art greeted the viewer, followed by reassurance of scholarly analysis; but far from controversy, the temple of muses certified that all was cultural. There was no illusion about that.

If commitment to the political and ideological framework of the contemporary arts is implicit in these seemingly raunchy examples, and in those cited from the beginning of this account, it is quite explicit in the bulk of straightforward productions of Art-art: the films of Jean-Luc Godard, the concerts of Karlheinz Stockhausen, the dances of Merce Cunningham, the buildings of Louis Kahn, the sculpture of Donald Judd, the paintings of Frank Stella, the novels of William Burroughs, the plays of Jerzy Grotowski, the mixed-media performances of E.A.T.—to mention a few well-known contemporaries and events of achievement. It is not that some of them are "abstract" and this is their Art, or that others have appropriate styles or subjects. It is that they rarely if ever played renegade with the profession of art *itself*. Their achievement, much of it in the recent past, was perhaps due to a conscious and poignant stance taken against an erosion of their respective fields by emerging non-artists. Perhaps it was mere innocence, or the narrow-mindedness of their professionalism. In any event, they upheld the silent rule that as a password *in,* "Art" is the best word of all.

It is questionable, however, whether it is worthwhile being "in." As a human goal and as an idea, Art is dying. Not just because it operates within conventions that have ceased to be fertile. It is dying because it has preserved its conventions and created a growing weariness toward them, out of indifference to what I suspect has become the fine arts' most important, though mostly unconscious, subject matter: *the ritual escape from culture.* Non-art as it changes into Art-art is at least interesting in the process. But Art-art, which starts out as such, short-cuts the ritual and feels from the very beginning merely cosmetic, merely a superfluous luxury, when such qualities do not in fact concern its makers at all.

Art-art's greatest challenge, in other words, has come from within its own heritage, from a hyperconsciousness about itself and about its everyday surroundings. Art-art has served as an instructional transition to its own elimination by life. Such an acute awareness among artists enables the whole world and its humanity to be experienced as a work of art. With ordinary reality so brightly lit, anyone who chooses to engage in showcase creativity invites (from this view) hopeless comparisons between what he does and supervivid counterparts in the environment.

Exemption from this larger ballpark is impossible. Art-artists, in spite of declarations that their work is not to be compared with life, will invariably be compared with non-artists. And, since non-art derives its fragile inspiration from everything *except* art, i.e., from "life," the comparison between Art-art and life will be made anyway. It then could be shown that, willingly or not, there has been an active exchange between Art-art and non-art, and in some cases between Art-art and the big wide world (in more than the translational way all art has utilized "real" experience). Relocated by our minds in a global setting rather than in a museum, library, or on stage, Art, no matter how it is arrived at, fares very badly indeed.

For example, La Monte Young, whose performances of complex drone sounds interest me as Art-art, tells of his boyhood in the Northwest when he used to lean his ear against the high-tension electric towers that stretched across the fields; he would enjoy feeling the hum of the wires through his body. I did that as a boy, too, and prefer it to the concerts of Young's music. Compared with a loft space or performance hall, it was more impressive visually and less hackneyed in the vastness of its environment.

For another non-art example, Dennis Oppenheim describes how in Canada he ran across a muddy lot, made plaster casts of his footprints (in the manner of a crime investigator), and then exhibited stacks of the casts at a gallery. The activity was great; the exhibition part of it was corny. The casts could have been left at the local police station without identification. Or thrown away.

> When anyone wishes to be called an artist, in order to have some or all of his acts and ideas considered art, he only has to drop an artistic thought around them, announce the fact, and persuade others to believe it. That's advertising. As Marshall McLuhan once wrote, "Art is what you can get away with."

Art. There's the catch. At this stage of consciousness, the sociology of culture emerges as an in-group "dumb show." Its sole audience is a roster of the creative and performing professions, watching itself, as if in a mirror, enact a struggle between self-appointed priests and a cadre of equally self-appointed commandos, jokers, gutter-snipers, and triple agents who seem to be attempting to destroy the priests' church. But everyone knows how it all ends: in church, of course, with the whole club bowing their heads and muttering prayers. They pray for themselves and for their religion.

Artists cannot profitably worship what is moribund; nor can they alternatively war against such bowing and scraping when only moments later they enshrine their destructions and acts as cult objects in the same institution they were bent on destroying. This is a patent sham. A plain case of management takeover.

But if artists are reminded that nobody but themselves gives a damn about this, or about whether all agree with the judgment here, then the entropy of the whole scene may begin to appear very funny.

Seeing the situation as low comedy is a way out of the bind. I would propose that the first practical step toward laughter is to *un-art* ourselves, avoid all aesthetic roles, give up all references to being artists of any kind whatever. In becoming "un-artists" (password four) we may only exist as fleetingly as the non-artist, for when the profession of art is discarded, the art category is meaningless, or at least antique. An un-artist is one who is engaged in changing jobs, in modernizing.

The new job does not entail becoming a naïf by beating a quick retreat back to childhood and yesterday. To the contrary, it requires even more sophistication than the un-artist has already. Instead of the serious tone that usually has accompanied the search for innocence and truth, un-arting probably will emerge as humor. This is where the old-fashioned saint in the desert and the new-fangled playboy of the jetways part company. The job implies fun, never gravity or tragedy.

Of course, in starting from the arts, the *idea* of art cannot easily be gotten rid of (even if one wisely never utters the word). But it is quite possible to shift the whole un-artistic operation slyly away from where the arts customarily congregate. To become, for instance, an account executive, an ecologist, a stunt rider, a politician, a beach bum. In these different capacities, the several kinds of art discussed would operate indirectly as a stored code, which, instead of programming a specific course of behavior, would facilitate an attitude of deliberate playfulness toward all professionalizing activities well beyond art. Signal scrambling, perhaps. Something like those venerable baseball aficionados in the vaudeville act that began, "Who's on first?" "No, Watt's on first; Hugh's on second . . ."

When someone anonymous called our attention recently to his or her slight transformation of a tenement stairway, and another directed us to examine an unaltered part of New York's Park Avenue, these were art, too. Whoever the persons were, they got the message to us (artists). We did the rest in our heads.

SAFE BETS FOR YOUR MONEY

It can be pretty well predicted that the various forms of mixed media or assemblage arts will increase, both in the highbrow sense and in mass-audience applications such as light shows, space-age demonstrations at world fairs, teaching aids, sales displays, toys, and political campaigns. And these may be the means by which all the arts are phased out.

While public opinion accepts mixed media as additions to the pantheon, or as new occupants around the outer edges of the expanding universe of each traditional medium, it is more likely that they are rituals of escape from the traditions. Given the historical thrust of the modern arts toward specialism or "purity"—pure painting, pure poetry, pure music, pure dance—any admixtures have had to be viewed as contaminants. And in this context, *deliberate* contamination can now be interpreted as a rite of passage. (It is noteworthy in this context that even at this late date there are no journals devoted to mixed media.)

Among the artists involved in mixed means during the last decade, a few became interested in taking advantage of the arts' blurry boundaries by going the next step toward blurring art as a whole into a number of non-arts. Dick Higgins, in his book *foew&ombwhnw* (New York: Something Else Press, 1969), describes in many instructive examples how vanguardists have taken positions between theatre and painting, poetry and sculpture, music and philosophy, and between various intermedia (his term), game theory, sports, and politics.

Abbie Hoffman applied the intermedium of Happenings (via the Provos) to a philosophical and political goal two or three summers ago. With a group of friends, he went to the observation balcony of the New York Stock Exchange. At a signal they tossed handfuls of dollar bills onto the floor below where trading was at its height. According to his report, brokers cheered, dived for the bills, the ticker tape stopped, the market was probably affected, and the press covered the event's conclusion as the cops arrived. Later that night, it appeared nationally on televised news coverage: a medium sermon "for the hell of it" as Hoffman might say.

It makes no difference whether this is called activism, criticism, pranksterism, self-advertisement, or art. Intermedia implies fluidity and simultaneity of roles. When art is only one of several possible functions a situation may have, it loses its privileged status and becomes, so to speak, a lower-case attribute. The intermedial response can be applied to anything, say an old glass. The glass can serve the geometrist to explain ellipses, the historian as an index to the technology of a past age, a painter for a still life and the gourmet to drink his Chateau Latour '53. We are not used to thinking like this, all at once, or nonhierarchically, but the intermedialist does it naturally. Context rather than category. Flow rather than work of art.

It follows that the conventions of painting, music, architecture, dance, poetry, theatre, and so on, may survive in a marginal capacity as academic researches, like the study of Latin. Aside from these analytic and curatorial uses, every sign points to their obsolescence. By the same token, galleries and museums, bookshops and libraries, concert halls, stages, arenas, and places of worship will be limited to the conservation of antiquities; that is, to what was done in the name of art up to about 1960.

Agencies for the spread of information by way of the mass media, and for the instigation of social activities, will become the new channels of insight and communication; not substituting for the classic "art experience" (however many things that may have been) but offering former artists compelling ways of participating in structured processes that can reveal new values, including the value of fun.

In this respect, the technological pursuits of today's non-artists and un-artists will multiply as industry, government, and education provide their resources. "Systems" technology involving the interfacing of personal and group experiences, instead of "product" technology, will dominate the trend. Software, in other words. But it will be a systems approach that favors an openness toward outcome, in contrast to the literal and goal-oriented uses now employed by most systems specialists. Like the childhood pastime "Telephone" (in which friends in a circle whisper a few words into one ear after the other only to hear them come out delightfully different when the last person says them aloud), the feedback loop is the model. Playfulness and the playful use of technology suggest a positive interest in acts of continuous discovery. Playfulness can become in the near future a social and psychological benefit.

A global network of simultaneously transmitting and receiving "TV Arcades." Open to the public twenty-four hours a day, like any washerette. An arcade in every big city of the world. Each equipped with one hundred or more monitors of different sizes from a few inches to wall-scale, in planar and irregular surfaces. A dozen automatically moving cameras (like those secreted in banks and airports, but now prominently displayed) will pan and fix anyone or thing that happens to come along or be in view. Including cameras and monitors if no one is present. A person will be free to do whatever he wants, and will see himself on the monitors in different ways. A crowd of people may multiply their images into a throng.

But the cameras will send the same images to all *other* arcades, at the same time or after a programmed delay. Thus what happens in one arcade may be happening in a thousand, generated a thousand times. But the built-in program for distributing the signals, visible and audible, random and fixed, could also be manually altered at any arcade. A woman might want to make electronic love to a particular man she saw on a monitor. Controls would permit her to localize (freeze) the communication within a few television tubes. Other visitors to the same arcade may feel free to enjoy and even enhance the mad and surprising scramble by turning their dials accordingly. The world could make up its own social relations as it went along. Everybody in and out of touch all at once!

P.S. This is obviously not art, since by the time it was realized nobody would remember that I wrote it here, thank goodness.

And what about art criticism? What happens to those keen interpreters who are even rarer than good artists? The answer is that in the light of the preceding, critics will be as irrelevant as the artists. Loss of one's vocation, however, may be only partial, since there is much to be done in connoisseurship and related scholarly endeavors in the universities and archives. And nearly all critics hold teaching posts anyway. Their work may simply shift more toward historical investigation and away from the ongoing scene.

But some critics may be willing to un-art themselves along with their artist colleagues (who just as often are professors and double as writers themselves). In this case, all their aesthetic assumptions will have to be systematically uncovered and dumped, together with all the historically loaded art terminology. Practitioners and commentators—the two occupations probably will merge, one person performing interchangeably—will need an updated language to refer to what is going on. And the best source of this, as usual, is street talk, news shorthand, and technical jargon.

For example, Al Brunelle, a few years back, wrote of the hallucinogenic surfaces of certain contemporary paintings as "skin freak." Even though the pop drug scene has changed since, and new words are necessary, and even though this article is not concerned with paintings, Brunelle's phrase is much more informative than such older words as *"tâche"* or "track," which also refer to a painting's surface. Skin freaking brought to picture-making an intensely vibrating eroticism that was particularly revealing for the time. That the experience is fading into the past simply suggests that good commentary can be as disposable as the artifacts in our culture. Immortal words are appropriate to immortal dreams.

Jack Burnham, in his book *Beyond Modern Sculpture* (New York: Braziller, 1968), is quite conscious of this need for accurate terms, and attempts to replace vitalist, formalist, and mechanistic metaphors with labels from science and technology like "cybernetics," "responsive systems," "field," "automata," etc. Yet these are compromised because the references are still "sculpture" and "art." To be thorough, such pietistic categories would have to be rejected totally.

In the long run, criticism and commentary as we know them may be unnecessary. During the recent "age of analysis" when human activity was seen as a symbolic smoke screen that had to be probed, explanations and interpretations were in order. But nowadays the modern arts themselves have become commentaries, and may forecast the "post-artistic age." They comment on their respective pasts, in which, for instance, the medium of television comments on the film; a live sound played alongside of its taped version comments on which is the "real"; one artist comments on another's latest moves; some artists comment on the state of their health or of the world; others comment on not commenting (while critics comment on all commentaries as I'm commenting here). This may be sufficient.

The most important short-range prediction that can be made has been inferred over and over again in the foregoing; that the actual, probably global, environment will engage us in an increasingly participational way. The environment will not be the "Environments" we are familiar with already: the constructed fun house, spook show, window display, storefront, and obstacle course. These have been sponsored by art galleries and discothèques. Instead, we'll act in response to the given natural and urban environments such as the sky, the ocean floor, winter resorts, motels, the movements of cars, the public services, and the communications media . . .

Preview of a 2001-Visual-of-the-U.S.A.-Landscape-Via-Supersonic-Jet. Every seat on the jet is equipped with monitors showing the earth below as the plane speeds over it. Choice of pictures in infrared, straight color, black-and-white; singly or in combination on various parts of the screen. Plus zoom-lens and stop-action controls.

Scenes from other trips are retrievable for flashback cuts and contrasts. Past comments on present. Selector lists: *Hawaiian Volcanos, The Pentagon, A Harvard Riot Seen When Approaching Boston, Sun Bathing on a Skyscraper.*

Audio hookup offers nine channels of prerecorded criticism of the American scene: two channels of light criticism, one of pop criticism and six channels of heavy criticism. There is also a channel for recording one's own criticism on a take-home video cassette documenting the entire trip.

P.S. This, also, is not art, because it will be available to too many people.

Artists of the world, drop out! You have nothing to lose but your professions!

EDUCATING ARTISTS *

Harold Rosenberg

. . . .

*"The limits of university training of artists"
writes Harold Rosenberg in this essay "need
to be rigorously analyzed not only by educators but by artists and others who understand
the intellectual nature of art." In effect, Rosenberg implies that art education is too important a subject to be left entirely to the whims
and devices of art educators. "The function of
the university is to impart knowledge, but art
is not solely knowledge . . . art is also ignorance and the eager consciousness of the unknown that impels creation." And he goes on
to note: "Ignorance . . . is not a quality a
university is equipped to supply or even to
honor."*

*Rosenberg criticizes an emphasis on techno-
logical aspects in art teaching because such
problems are not very important anymore.
"The most backward ideas in art teaching today are the idea of inspiration and the accompanying notion that the teacher need only
provide the technical training needed to express that inspiration."*

* Reprinted from *The New Yorker*, Vol. XLV, No. 13 (May 17, 1969) .

However there is a lot to be taught, he claims. "Art is a specialization . . . Its data can be taught, as the data of any specialization can be taught."

Rosenberg doesn't expect change to come very quickly in artistic education, and he believes that before the major problems are solved ". . . even the most ineffective faculty member will have had ample time to live out his tenure in peace." He concludes that today ". . . art has become the study and practice of culture in its active day-to-day life."

Harold Rosenberg, art critic for The New Yorker, *is author of several books on art, including* Tradition of the New *(New York: Mc-Graw-Hill, 1965) and* The Anxious Object *(New York: Mentor Press, 1969).*

. . . .

Though outsiders might not suspect it, the training of students in universities to be painters and sculptors is an extremely touchy subject not only in educational circles but in the art world as well. Almost any suggestion or critical comment threatens existing interests, often invisible to the critic. Even mention of the fact that the typical artist today has been educated in a university is sufficient to provoke outcries. At a conference not long ago on cultural changes in the Americas since the war, I emphasized the shift of art training from professional schools and artists' studios. My mere citing of some figures—for example, only one of ten leading artists of the generation of Jackson Pollock and Willem de Kooning had a degree (and not in art), while of the "thirty artists under thirty-five" shown in "Young America 1965" at the Whitney Museum of American Art in New York the majority had B.A.s or B.F.A.s—was taken by a prominent younger painter as implying that he and his age group were academic. "Academic" is still a bad word, even though no one knows any longer exactly what it means. Perhaps the term that used to designate ennobled nudes ought not be applied to carefully calculated dispositions of parallel lines or patterns of color. For my own part, I am willing to drop "academic" and substitute "conceptual"—a term to which younger artists have no objection. My point was only that a new source of instruction for artists will affect their attitudes toward art, their handling of materials, and, ultimately, the styles in which they choose to work. Can there be any doubt that training in the university has contributed to the cool, impersonal wave in the art of the sixties? In the classroom—in contrast to the studio, which has tended to be dominated by metaphor—it is normal to formulate consciously what one is doing and to be able to explain it to others. Creation is taken to be synonymous with productive processes, and is broken down into sets of problems and solutions. In a statement, published in a pamphlet sponsored by several foundations, on *The Arts and the Contemporary University,* Dr. Martin Meyerson, president of the State University of New York at Buffalo, noted the "tremendous production emphasis [that] pervades much of the university's work in the arts." New painting and sculpture typical of the past decade make the spectator aware of the presence of model works that have been not so much imitated or drawn upon for imaginative hints as systematically analyzed and extended by rational inference. For instance, Josef Albers' impacted-color squares have become the basis of impacted-color rectangles, chevrons, circles, stripes—works bred out of works, often without the intervention of a new vision. In the shift from bohemia to academe, American art has become more conceptual, methodological, and self-assured. So pointing to the university training of today's artists very likely does carry a criticism.

If merely noting the new university connections of art can be regarded as an insult, far more menacing is any inquiry into who is teaching what, and how. Or what relation there is between an academic degree and the capacity to function as an artist in the last third of the twentieth century. Dr. William Schuman, former president of Lincoln Center, calls for art training that will "produce practitioners," and then at once complains that "there are innumerable campuses where there are second-rate artists who give nothing but their own point of view to students." First-rate artists also tend to give their own point of view, and while this may at least be a valuable, or at any rate interesting, experience, it will not always suffice to meet the needs of art study. Dr. Schuman may have had in mind that a good teacher will present all relevant points of view, but in painting and sculpture the first-rate artist is the least likely to do this. My own observations of the quality of artists on campuses support those of Dr. Schuman, and I shall present additional testimony on the second-rate later. Yet to say that most artists now teaching in universities haven't much to contribute either to art or to their students threatens not only their jobs but the entire position of art in the university—a position still highly infirm, despite the advances of the last fifteen years. Dr. Samuel B. Gould, chancellor of the State University of New York, who believes in the future of art in the universities, recognizes that there are still educators who "earnestly and sincerely" doubt that art production has any place in higher education, and Dr. Meyerson says that "in common rooms and faculty clubs, it [art] is often referred to as 'hobby lobby' or [*sic*] other terms of opprobrium." Given this opposition, deans are hardly likely to be eager to allocate funds to enlist faculty members publicly character-ized as second-rate; comparable questions are not raised about mediocre art historians.

If good artists are needed to teach art, the situation seems irremediable. Where are art departments to obtain first-rate artists willing to spend their time teaching, especially in colleges remote from art centers? And, thus isolated, how long would those artists remain first-rate? Is there even any agreement—except upon a handful of names, perhaps—about who is first-rate? Beyond the quality of the teacher, there is the problem that art changes almost from season to season in outlook, concept, and even the materials out of which it is made. If the subject being taught could be defined, the matter of whether those who teach it are first- or second-rate might be less important. As it is, even if the quality of an artist's work is beyond dispute, an attempt by him to encompass each new move in the art world makes him, as a teacher, in effect second-rate, since only the inventor of the new move is first-rate in relation to it. (I would not have expected to learn much about the art of Andy Warhol in a class conducted by Alberto Giacometti.) Ambitious students are apt to be aware of this situation; no matter how distinguished the creations of their artist-teacher, they regard him as inadequate to impart the latest mode popular in New York. Speaking recently to a university audience, Jack Tworkov, chairman of the Art Department at Yale, observed that the students in his department (in my opinion, the best in the United States) scarcely listen to their teachers but derive their ideas from the art journals.

Failing to make up their minds that art teaching is their business, the universities have been content to let matters drift. Still engaged in agitating for administrative support, advocates of art in the universities tremble at the thought of confronting the problems of teaching it. Any speaker who raises questions of direction at con-

ferences of the College Art Association is met with nods
and silence. Debates likely to disrupt one's own side are
taken to be less useful than clichés designed to hold off
the enemy. According to Dr. Gould, "the major reason"
educators remain uncertain about admitting artist training into the universities "is that so much of what one
wishes to deal with in the arts touches upon technique
as opposed to philosophy." To overcome the doubt of
his colleagues, Dr. Gould presents an idealized version
of the artist-on-campus as "the whole man" whom humanity is in danger of losing in the face of the growing
mass of "insensitive specialists" turned out by the sciences. Generous to art as Dr. Gould's outlook is, I am
unable to agree that only scientists produce works "un-
intelligible to the uninitiated." Art today is as specialized and esoteric as the sciences, and, the way it is being
taught, much of it does "touch upon technique" rather
than philosophy. Studio courses are a kind of vocational
training that swings from extremes of avant-gardism (experiments with light, film, electronics, synthetics, computers) to extremes of standing pat on whatever technique the instructor has been practicing as an artist. Having called attention to the second-raters, Dr. Schuman
goes on to refer to a famous college "where students are
either given the music of the sixteenth century or John
Cage but almost nothing in between," and he speaks of
another school, "equally distinguished, where the music
of John Cage is not even permitted to be mentioned."
The situation in painting is identical: either Minimal-
ism, earthworks, lights—or copying Renaissance masters,
drawing from casts, painting Impressionist interiors. Between these two orientations, everything taught depends
on the chance of finding the best-known artist who happens to be available. The conservative/avant-garde po-
larization reflects the deep division in modern culture;
restricted to the level of techniques, the conflict serves as

a substitute for a coherent concept of art in our time. Dr. Gould's doubters are correct, and if art teaching remains what it is, perhaps the art workshops do not belong on campus—though one could reply that most subjects taught in universities today touch upon "technique as opposed to philosophy."

image of the artist as creator, the actual education of the
While advocates of art in the universities invoke the student as artist is indistinguishable from that of the commercial designer. The formation, five years ago of the New York Studio School of Drawing, Painting, and Sculpture came about through the revolt of students in a degree-granting institution against courses unrelated to the vocation of artist. In a speech describing the founding of the School, Mercedes Matter, chairman of the faculty, exposed the absurdity of training painters by depriving them of the opportunity to paint. Remembering the earlier enslavement of its students, the Studio School has made a fetish of not awarding degrees. Its solution of the problem of educating artists was to return to the old verities of the art academy: continuous drawing, painting, and modeling, contact with older artists, reliance on "the gift, the temperament, the purpose." Opposing the "practical" emphasis of university art courses, Mrs. Matter insists that art is "a perfectly useless activity." (She might have added that it is also a nostalgic one, since, deprived of the heroic concept of masterpieces, it tends to blend into the communications and entertainment media.)

Taking advantage of the availability of New York artists, museums, and galleries, the Studio School avoids the mental and psychic fragmentation of the typical college art department, and its teaching is a match for all but the best. Since it relies entirely on the individual teachings of artists, it fails, however, to advance the problem of proper training for an artist today, to say nothing of his education in general. Mrs. Matter's argument that Fernand Léger, Giacometti, de Kooning, Philip Guston were able to dispense with universities, "thanks to their high degree of intelligence and curiosity," is beside the point; the function of an educator is to educate, not to hope that lack of education will be compensated for by the student's natural gifts. In the Studio School, applying paint to canvas and talking about painting are accepted as sufficient preparation for a creative response to the contemporary world. The weakness of this position is revealed in the fact that the School has found itself forced into a blanket rejection of current developments in art. "I frankly don't understand anti-art or the causes of the present scene," confesses Mrs. Matter, apparently unaware that art education means precisely to impart to art students the ability to encompass the "present scene" with critical comprehension. In her statement there are indications that she mistakes art for holiness, as when she finds offering an art student a course in commercial design as absurd as teaching a young nun the art of streetwalking. That the art student is entering upon a sacred calling is also intimated by her belief that "an artist can do nothing to influence his own work"—a contention that would eliminate the need for any kind of education. To make up for its innate conservatism, the Studio School, in typical art-department vanguard-mongering, has announced a seminar this summer by Buckminster Fuller on the "World Game."

Another critic of university art courses is Dan Flavin, a sculptor whose medium is fluorescent light tubes; his diatribe in *Artforum* last March, "On an American Artist's Education," was a brilliant and cruel attack—it could not have been brilliant without being cruel—on the concepts and categories of teachers responsible for university "indoctrination of students in art historical media."

Flavin's article is a detailed polemic against Dr. Schuman's art workshops manned by second-rate artists, and he seems to agree with Mrs. Matter that "a college degree in art is a certificate of the fact that its recipient has not been studying art at such-and-such a place for four years." In his opinion, university studio teaching is largely dominated by "aging refugees from the commercial art game" who deliver "trade courses such as design, lithography, or art history" (censored, he notes) to students working for degrees that will license them to transmit to others their own lack of understanding of art. By Flavin's testimony, all modes of art, from the most retrograde drawings of "humanists" to the latest avant-garde "fun things," are being taught as a technique, the sum of which will constitute an art education. Lacking unity of purpose, the mediums are taught in isolation from one another, and decisions in the art departments are determined by careerism and the struggles of factions.

Flavin's criticism is biting and realistic, but it fails to offer a new approach to university art teaching. Despite his acrimony, he prefers—in contrast to the Studio School —the human product of the university to the disorderly, intellectually groping artist of an earlier time. "The romance of days of belabored feeling," he writes, "of precious, pious, compulsively grimy studio-bound labor by haphazardly informed neurotic 'loners,' often verging on mental illness, relying desperately on intuitive good sense, is passing from art. The contemporary artist is becoming a public man, trusting his own intelligence, confirming his own informed ideas." This sounds hardheaded and forward-looking, though not exactly new; fifty years ago, the Constructivists and the Bauhaus also conceived of the new artist as a sophisticated, healthy, self-confident professional—a "public man" who, like the lawyer or engineer, confirms "his own informed ideas." It is pleasant, of course, to meet well-educated painters and sculptors instead of the farmer or artisan types to which many artists, especially sculptors, used to belong. The contemporary sculptor who inscribes instructions and a loose sketch on a sheet of blueprint paper and sends it to the foundry for execution is a man of words and mathematical symbols, a cross between a poet and an engineer, and you don't get people like that without intellectual training—I mean, as opposed to training with paintbrushes, hammers, and chisels, and other messy materials. But if "intuitive good sense" is not to be relied on, it is difficult to see where Flavin's new-style artist can obtain his informed ideas except in the university. Flavin's essay is a model of that systematic packaging of artists, teachers, and art modes that prevails in college teaching. He repudiates this categorizing when it is applied to him ("no significant attempt was ever made to probe my thinking as an artist," he exclaims indignantly when a college instructor rejects his fluorescent sculpture on the ground that it is technologically surpassed by programmed lights), but he seems not to realize that "probing" another artist's thinking belongs among the habits of self-education of that old, now passé loner, and his own outlook is that of the avant-garde wing of art-department technical training.

If art teaching in the university is to be improved, the first requisite is to deal with its problems candidly and without excessive delicacy; before these problems are solved, even the most ineffective faculty member will have had ample time to live out his tenure in peace. The limits of university training of artists need to be rigorously analyzed not only by educators but by artists and others who understand the intellectual nature of art. The function of the university is to impart knowledge, but art is not solely knowledge and the problems proposed by knowledge; art is also ignorance and the eager consciousness of the unknown that impels creation. No matter how cultivated he is, every artist is in some degree a naïf, a primitive, and relies on his particular gift of ignorance. It is the undeveloped, perhaps unacknowledged areas of the mind that art counts on, even in its most rational aspects. That combination of ignorance, enthusiasm, intuition, and inventiveness cannot be put together for each member of a university course, nor is it the business of the university teacher to attempt it. Ignorance in particular is not a quality a university is equipped to supply, or even to honor.

Since it cannot teach all the elements of creation, art education must concentrate on what can be taught. This teachable matter is far more extensive than is generally supposed. An enormous volume of significant information about works of art and their mode of generation has been accumulated in this century, and the failure to open this to the student deprives him of the only currently available equivalent of the atelier. The most backward ideas in art teaching today are the idea of inspiration and the accompanying notion that the teacher need only provide the technical training needed to express that inspiration. Art as an inspired craft belongs to the preindustrial era. The history of modern art is a history of varieties of means developed by artists artificially to induce inspiration, including the vigorous denial of any need for it. Art is a specialization, even when it is a specialization of spirit. Its data can be taught, as the data of any specialization can be taught.

In overstressing technique, both the fundamentalists and the avant-gardists in teaching mistake the nature of art in our time. Despite modern technological self-consciousness, art in the twentieth century is technical to a lesser degree than it was in the age of the potter's wheel or the maulstick. As Adolph Gottlieb has remarked, any artist with an idea will find out how to execute it; on the other hand, artists develop ideas through unfocused playing with their medium. The basic substance of art has become the protracted discourse in words and materials echoed back and forth from artist to artist, work to work, art movement to art movement, on all aspects of contemporary civilization and of the place of creation and of the individual in it. The student-artist needs, while learning to see and execute, above all to be brought into this discourse, without which the history of modern painting and sculpture appears a gratuitous parade of fashions. What used to be called talent has become subsidiary to insight into significant developments and possibilities. In a word, art has become the study and practice of culture in its active day-to-day life. Begin by explaining a single contemporary painting (and the more apparently empty of content it is the better), and if you continue describing it you will find yourself touching on more subjects to investigate—philosophical, social, political, historical, scientific, psychological—than are needed for an academic degree.

Part Three

. . . .

ART HISTORY
IN
THE COLLEGE

Patricia Sloan

TEACHING ART HISTORY
IN THE COMMUNITY COLLEGE *

Patricia Sloan

. . . .

"The true answer for education in a democracy is not to make the same garbage available to everybody but to improve the level of educational consumables."

So writes Patricia Sloan, who examines, in this straightforward and outspoken article, some traditional values in popular education. She doesn't like very much of what she finds.

As far as art history is concerned, she feels it ". . . is either dead or else never was fully alive"; as a field of study she finds it ". . . conceptually chaotic and untidy." Today, such ideas are being taken seriously by many younger scholars in the field; this paper may be considered a manifesto on the subject by some.

More and more teachers are finding the conventional "art appreciation" approach to art teaching repugnant. Sloan notes: "As for teaching students to 'appreciate' art, this pernicious activity is beneath contempt for any honest teacher." And she examines the bias for

* Paper read at the 1972 Annual Meeting of the College Art Association, San Francisco, Calif., January 1972.

Western European art found in most texts. Her conclusions parallel observations of Black- and third-world oriented educational writers and critics.

Finally she calls for a complete restructuring of the basic survey course in art history, and offers several suggestions.

Pat Sloan is the author of Color: Basic Principles *(New York: Van Nostrand Reinhold, 1968), and teaches art history at New York City Community College.*

. . . .

The question of how art history ought to be taught in two-year colleges reduces finally to the question of how to teach a general survey course covering the entire history of art. Few two-year colleges offer a full spectrum of more highly specialized courses.

Survey courses in art history are bad for the same reason that survey courses in any subject are bad. Too much material is supposed to be covered in too short a time and in too superficial a manner. The net result is that students learn very little except how to mouth a series of clichés. The ubiquitous survey course, in art history and in other subjects as well, comprises a good part of the substance of a liberal arts education. That we have offered the opportunity to acquire this type of education—this assimilation of trivia—to Black, Puerto Rican, and other disadvantaged students in the community colleges is probably less of a favor than many of the students naïvely suppose. The true answer for education in a democracy is not to make the same garbage available to everybody but to improve the level of educational consumables.

As a discipline art history is either dead or else never

was fully alive. It is too much out of touch with art and too much out of touch with history. As a field of study it is conceptually chaotic and untidy, not because there are so many art-historical facts to deal with but because art historians as a group are disinclined to examine their own intellectual prejudices, limitations, and assumptions. Although there have been a few hopeful stirrings recently, art history has traditionally neither studied its own history nor analyzed its presuppositions. Historians, by comparison with art historians, cultivate a different attitude, and since the time of Thucydides have been in the habit of stepping back from their work to ask themselves what they think they are doing. On account of this self-examination there is even a body of literature dealing with what might be called the philosophy of history. There is no philosophy of art history, a study that winds its unwitting way onward caring neither where it is going nor where it has been.

One problem in teaching a general survey of art history is that there may be no such thing as a coherently envisioned "general" history of art. And there is little interest in developing one. Art history today is a field in which all the workers are specialists and there are no generalists. Perhaps there is even a lack of understanding on the point that a generalist is something other than a specialist on everything. Books dealing with the general history of art are written to accommodate laymen and beginning students and are of no interest whatever to scholars. Perhaps this is why such books do not attain a more satisfactory level of scholarship. In his capacity as a researcher and thinker each art historian does his own specialized thing in his own special specialized area. Each either hopes or assumes that his specialized studies will fit together in some sensible way with other people's specialized studies. But if one man had studied horses, another cows, and another chickens the sum total of these

isolated and somewhat precious investigations would not
necessarily have constituted what we today know as biology. The Linnaean system of classification used in biology
is far superior to the system of stylistic classification used
in art history. This is only because greater attention has
been given by biologists to analysis (and not merely collection) of data and to examination of their field as a
whole. Perhaps there is only one thing that students
ought to know about art-historical cataloguing and style
names. They ought to know that the overall system of
art-historical style names is not very well thought out,
and the names are sometimes not used in the same way
by different authors. For some commentators Early Chris-
tian art means art produced in Western Europe before
the end of the fifth century. For others the Early Chris-
tian period extends through the sixteenth century and
may also include the art of the Byzantines. Some art-historical style names (e.g., Egyptian art) refer to a country.
Others (e.g., High Renaissance art) refer to a historical
period. Others (e.g., Ottoman art) refer to a political
dynasty. Still others (Cubism, Impressionism) are nick-
names that somehow or other stuck. Sometimes Black
students tell me that it is an outrage for the art of Black
Africa to be called Primitive art. I do not know what to
tell them except that the entire system of art-historical
classification is an outrage and perhaps some day someone will give some thought to improving it.

Graduate students of art history sometimes complain
that there are no specialties left in which they might
concentrate since every area has been studied. This view
is remarkably naïve. There is no oversupply of books on
Tibetan painting, Bushman art, Indian bronzes, or Russian architecture. There is only an excessive emphasis
on the art of Western Europe.

In most colleges the survey class in art history has
acquired the reputation of being a rote memorization

"names and dates" class. Some educators ask if there is any value in requiring students to remember names and dates. They suggest as alternatives that students be taught such things as concepts, "feeling," and "appreciation." I do not believe this is where the problems really lie. Students have no difficulty remembering the names of artists if they are given sufficient opportunity to discuss and analyze artworks, either through viewing slides or through museum visits. Remembering names only becomes a problem if the students are required to commit to memory too many and if they have not seen sufficient slides to have a clear idea of what some particular artist's work looks like. Whenever it is possible to do so I structure individual class sessions around the work of a single artist. One lecture on Leonardo, one on Raphael, and two on Michelangelo (one dealing with the Sistine Chapel ceiling) tell beginning students what they need to know about the High Renaissance in Italy. I do not approve of lectures which bypass artists to talk about periods. The general statements one can make about the "characteristics" of the High Renaissance in Italy are primarily catchphrases and vacuities. If students remember only that the High Renaissance is the period when Leonardo, Michelangelo, and Raphael worked—and if they can remember the work of these artists—this seems to be enough. If under the pretext of talking about a period students are shown the work of two dozen different artists, with one slide only for the work of each artist, of course there is difficulty about remembering names: It is always harder to remember the name of an artist one knows almost nothing about. The real question is why it is thought a virtue to force students to remember tediously long lists of the names of artists when there has not been time in class to tell them very much about the work of any of the artists whose names are on the list.

I show my students, for example, sixty slides of Rubens'

work, since this seems to be the most expeditious way of insuring that they remember what Rubens' work looks like. I do not expect them to remember the names of the sixty paintings, although some students remember some of them. At the beginning of the semester each student is given slide lists, one for each class meeting, which identify each slide to be shown and tell the date on which each artwork was made and the museum in which it can be seen. The purpose of these slide lists is to minimize note-taking in class. Students cannot look at and think about a slide while they are sitting in the dark trying to record the name of the artwork and other information about it. I tell students not to take many notes and to train themselves to remember what they see or what is talked about. But most of my students are very conservative and want to take notes anyway. I am thinking of compiling review notes to distribute to students along with the slide lists, because I strongly believe that the classroom should be a place for looking and thinking, not a place for note-taking. Review notes might also make it possible to dispense with a textbook for the class, which—given the texts that are available—I think would be an advantage.

If students are to be taught about art-historical concepts in some way that assumes that a concept is a meaningful entity in isolation from the work of artists, I am not sure how one could begin. The only "concept" there is to French Impressionism is that at a certain time and place a certain group of artists developed a particular way of making paintings. Whoever knows the paintings knows the concept, whether or not he calls it a concept. Whoever knows the concept without knowing the paintings—to the extent that such a thing is possible—really knows nothing at all.

As for teaching students to "appreciate" art, this pernicious activity is beneath contempt for any honest

teacher. It is only suitable for those instructors less interested in intellectual inquiry than in a defense of the
status quo. Teaching appreciation implies manipulating
the feelings of students, which is nothing other than
brainwashing. I cannot require that my students "learn
to like" Botticelli since this is inconsistent with requiring that they *think about* his work. If students are to
be taught to think about art, then as a result of this
thinking they are free to arrive at their own conclusions.
It is self-contradictory to set up the prior expectation
that all students must decide that they like all, or even
some, art. We cannot decide to teach taste to students,
since there is no single type of educated taste, although
there is a single type of conventional taste. And a good
teacher turns out students who think, not students who
think like their teacher.

Textbooks designed for use in an art history survey
course bear titles such as *History of Art* and *Art Through
the Ages*. A more precise description of the contents of
either of these texts would be given if they were called,
respectively, "History of Art in Western Europe" and
"Art Through the Ages, Primarily in Europe." A survey of art history ought to consist of a history of *world*
art, not a history of the development of Western European art. Even though no suitable text is available I
structure my own classes to emphasize not only the art of
Western Europe but also that of India, China, Japan,
Tibet, Mongolia, Eastern Europe including Russia and
the Balkans, Oceania, and Africa, as well as the art of
the indigenous peoples of North, South, and Central
America. The history of European art is not the history
of art, since it is not the history of *all* art. Confusing
"art" as a generic term with "European art" is only a
form of racism. It is a carry-over of the Victorian idea
that a single great mainstream of art and culture exists,
and that with the exception of a few peripheral peoples

(e.g., the Egyptians and the Byzantines) the contributors to this mainstream are exclusively white and of Western European ethnic origin. Today we know there is no single mainstream although the discovery is slow in filtering down to those who prepare textbooks on the history of art. Helen Gardner's *Art Through the Ages* (5th ed.; New York: Harcourt Brace Jovanovich, 1970), recently revised, even omits any mention of Islamic art. I do not know what this omission implies to students except perhaps that art is produced primarily in Europe and there is no need to take seriously those peoples who aren't Christians.

In the teaching of a survey course in art history the emphasis on European art is used to persuade students that there is some sort of great European art tradition that reached high points in classical Greece and during the Italian Renaissance. Apparently students are to believe that this great European tradition is better than anyone else's tradition since no one else's tradition is worth studying. "Yes, Johnny," we seem to be saying, "there is a white, civilized world and a mainstream of civilization." A biased presentation of this sort is obviously deeply offensive to those students who are not of European ethnic or racial origin. There are other objections to it that weigh even more heavily than the niceties of racial etiquette. I do not believe students should be led to suppose that art history is a dispassionate report of events, or that art-historical value judgments have traditionally been made according to objective standards. Art history is also the history of what people have thought about art, and therefore it is a history of changing tastes and continuing controversies. There are neither eternal standards nor unanimity of opinion. Alfred North Whitehead thought, if Gibbon did not, that Byzantine civilization reached a higher level than that of the Greeks. Frank Lloyd Wright thought the

Renaissance was a disaster. As for modern art, it would not exist at all if artists had not disassociated themselves from the naturalist norms by which we still gauge the level of the art produced in Western Europe from the days of Plato to the days of Queen Victoria. From the Impressionists and Postimpressionists with their Japanese prints to Pablo Picasso and Constantin Brancusi with their African carvings the early development of modern art is a story of confrontation between European and non-European aesthetics. This confrontation has been envisioned by some commentators as a flight on the part of European artists into primitivism or toward the exotic. As a corollary this flight into primitivism is also a flight *from* the Western European tradition of naturalism. No contemporary artist holds to the views of art first enunciated by Plato and later echoed by, for example, Nicolas Poussin.

If art history is to be taught as the history of world art, not as the history of art in Europe, one practical question is how this can be done since it is usually agreed that a survey course in art history already spans too great a range of material. My personal solution is to eliminate from the art history survey course any study whatever of architecture, including even the Parthenon and Gothic cathedrals. If the history of architecture is to receive anything other than superficial treatment, then it ought to be handled in a separate course apart from the history of art. The single exception to this exclusion of architecture is that I do give a lecture on the palace of King Minos at Knossos since Sir Arthur Evans' over-determined restorations of the building—which are quite obvious even in slides—proved useful for illustrating to students some of the problems that arise in conservation and restoration.

History, T. S. Eliot said, deceives us. Napoleon is supposed to have called history a fable written by the winning side. Perhaps it should be part of teaching the history of art to make students aware that the history of art is an illusion. Archaeologists, by comparison with art historians, seem to be graced with a more subtle sensibility about the nature of historical models. I do not presume to tell my students what impulse motivated prehistoric man to paint the walls of the Altamira caves. Instead I confine myself to explaining what the current theory is, making it clear that this is a theory, not a fact. Then I ask the students to invent other theories of their own, and to think about whether *any* of these conjectures are really susceptible to proof. The past is shattered fragments, and many of the fragments—we do not know how many—are lost beyond hope of recovery. We cannot transcend the lack of data by empathy since empathy is a fantasy of the empathizer.

Nothing is more revealing of art-historical attitudes about the nature of history than the familiar saw that art historians cannot study contemporary art because it is happening now. Art historians will analyze modern art—it is said—when the flux of its happening has subsided, providing a more favorable opportunity for dispassionate investigation. I presume it is common knowledge by now that some art historians see themselves as antiquarians, and are reluctant to deal with contemporary art because of an antipathy to it. What is even more interesting about the argument, however, is that it seems to imply that history is a body of data within which no lacunae exist. It seems to me that in a number of ways it is *easier* to study the present than the past since a greater amount of data is available, making it easier to separate the facts from the fictions. One can always call Robert Morris on the telephone and ask him to verify some point of fact about his sculpture. One cannot do this in the case of Michelangelo.

I believe in building art-historical models, but only if

it is remembered that these models are inventions, not discoveries. The past, to the extent that it is not merely a delusion of the present, lies on the other side of a temporal barrier as complete as that which separates us from the future. Whoever refuses to see that we cannot penetrate this barrier lacks either humility or common sense. In other words, teaching art history implies more than telling students what is known about the Egyptians and their art; it also implies making clear that there are many things we do not know about the Egyptians, and will probably never know.

I am not sympathetic to the modern idea—perhaps Jung should be credited with inventing its prototype— that history ought to be edited to create the impression that the particular matters of most concern to us today are exactly those that most interested all peoples at all times. Apparently this type of modern educational exegesis is inspired by an admirable but misguided intention to come to terms with student complaints about the irrelevance of studies in the humanities. The most relevant fact about history is that it *is* dead. I do not know why some people are unwilling to say so unless there is a reluctance to come to terms with the idea of death. I agree with Picasso that *works of art* do not die. This is only because works of art (unlike men) possess the capability of surviving, in a physical sense, from the past down into our own era. Chartres Cathedral still stands today, although its builders are dead. And art history involves more than merely looking at Chartres Cathedral; it implies an awareness of its builders. Teaching art history implies communicating information about dead people, including dead artists, who lived in dead societies that no longer exist. Why should we pretend they are still alive? Why should we insult the intelligence of young people by imagining it is they, not we, who want to engage in this type of pretense?

Perhaps there has been some misunderstanding about the nature of student complaints. But if young people are really asking—as I do not think they are—why they ought to be interested in peoples whose concerns and life-styles differed from their own, then the question has ominous undertones. And these truly dangerous and antisocial implications are not met by conjuring up some fantasy world in which everyone is, and always has been, just like everyone else. I hope the purpose of a survey class in art history is not merely to suggest that art, culture, and beliefs have always been essentially the same. It is equally true that they have always been different, and that diversity is a fact of art and life.

There are many possibilities for completely restructuring the basic survey course in art history. Perhaps classes should meet in museums and not in the classroom. Perhaps the course should be structured on an individual tutorial basis instead of through classroom lectures. Perhaps tests and final examinations are an inappropriate vehicle for gauging what an individual student has learned. Perhaps there ought to be more leeway for planning individual student projects, which combine art-historical study with related studio experience. Perhaps college curricula should be restructured to minimize fragmentation, permitting students to study one subject at a time, not four or five at once. Perhaps the survey course in art history ought to be taught—as it is in some community colleges—by painters instead of art historians. Since many of these possibilities are beyond the control of the individual teacher I have not discussed them here. They are all germane to a more extended discussion of how to improve the quality of a basic survey course in art history.

NEW WAYS OF TEACHING
ART HISTORY *

Irving Sandler

. . . .

In this article, Irving Sandler distinguishes between two major approaches, each calling for different methods, in the teaching of art history. The first involves the teaching of art history to art history students, and the other concerns the teaching of art history to studio students.

In both, Sandler advocates a revised format for the teaching of art history, with the initial emphasis on contemporary art, rather than the other way around. The idea, as the author points out, has already received acceptance at some forward-looking institutions. He supports the new, reversed chronology by citing the constant and unavoidable condition by which art of the past is revaluated by the present, and he advocates letting "the present regenerate those aspects of the past that illuminate and enrich the present."

The common acceptance of a linear chronology that governs the teaching of art his-

* Paper from the *Proceedings* of a Conference on Art Criticism and Art Education at the Guggenheim Museum, New York, May 15–16, 1970.

Irving Sandler. Photograph by Ann Johnson courtesy New York State Council of the Arts.

*tory inhibits authentic challenge in education
and does not encourage teachers to question
and renew values continually, according to
Sandler. However, he points out that he does
not see the need to disregard any aspect of art
history—only the questioning of priorities.*

*The role of the art critic, and the new "historian critic" is especially important because
". . . it is he who is most concerned with contemporary art and its conflicting and competing values."*

*Sandler teaches the History of Modern Art
at New York University. He has written criticism for* Art News, Art International, *and*
Artforum. *He is President of the American
Section of the International Association of Art
Critics.*

. . . .

The teaching of art history traditionally has been based
on a conception of the past as a more or less orderly
evolution of artistic traditions from generation to generation, each generation adding its gloss while considering those traditions valuable and pertinent to its time.

However, in our modern era, changes in art—as in
life—have been revolutionary rather than evolutionary.
Certainly, they can be viewed as evolutionary, when examined closely, but they have occurred at so rapid a
tempo and have proliferated in such a variety of directions that the cumulative effect is an extreme dislocation of past and present. History can no longer be treated
as a more or less continuous flow.

The dislocation of past and present has given rise to
a shift of focus, more pronounced than ever before, on
the here and now, on our contemporary culture, its

values and standards. This shift is compelling us to re-valuate the role of received humanistic values implicit in art history as it is generally being taught today.

To be sure, motivating much of modern art is the idea that these values are no longer viable, a point of view held more widely than ever before. With regard to art-historical curricula, however, there has been a time lag. Teachers of art history have generally either neglected or have given only token treatment to modern art; the common practice of those teaching survey courses is to jam it all in the final session.

Growing ever more urgent is the question: does the humanist tradition, which in the past was accepted as the fount of wisdom and the source of standards, continue to be valuable in illuminating the problems of our present as it opens into the future? As far as many students today are concerned, it is not. The world as they see it is a far more fragmented, random—even orderless and meaningless—place than the past allowed.

Gerald F. Else has remarked: "The old humanities represented selection, concentration, and community: a common, shared experience of a limited canon of great works . . . all educated men (in the West, that is: from Italy to Iceland) had had this common experience and could communicate with one another on the basis of it."

As if in dialogue with Else, C. Jon Roush has written:

. . . the culture that the conventional course in the humanities "transmits" is in many ways not the one that the students have actually inherited . . . For most undergraduates now . . . the house of the humanities seems not a sacred temple but a museum. In the anthropological sense of "culture" as a shared set of values, customs, and symbols, the artifacts in the humanities museum come from a culture radically foreign to the one in which the students have been reared and to which most of them are destined to return.

Like our students, many contemporary artists, in response to the revolutionary changes that have taken place in modern life, spurn as valueless any style that repeats what has been and does not radically transform or expand inherited conceptions of art. The very explosion in artistic tendencies in recent years is proof of this.

At its root, I think that the demand for relevance in education today is a demand that all tacitly accepted values be exposed and then that they be subjected to genuine challenge. The teacher is required to yield none of his beliefs but to forgo an authoritarian stance—any notion that he has the last word, and that his function is to indoctrinate by that word.

Instead, the classroom situation should become essentially an interaction of teachers and students. The emphasis should be upon the individual and his growth—a process of self-study in interaction with others. In this process, each individual would rationally test all of his preconceptions, rational and irrational, guiding his behavior, and more specifically, his perception of art, in an ambiance of competing judgments and be held responsible for his own choices, not the least of which would be the task of formulating his own past.

Roush has described two contrasting approaches to learning. He has called one the "syncretic tradition" in which "the past is important as a linear succession that we should be able to retrace to our roots." The other is the "dialectical tradition" in which "the past is a home for . . . living antagonists who can inspire, correct, or be corrected or rejected by us." If one accepts the "dialectical tradition," it follows "that the function of teachers and scholars is not to transmit but to challenge and be challenged . . . It suggests that their strategy is to give students opportunities for making significant choices and at the same time holding them responsible for the choices they have made."

It must be stressed that teachers should continually test and renew their values. It may be, as Margaret Mead maintains, that teachers have as much or more to learn from their students as they, the teachers, have to offer. She has said, probably overstating the case somewhat that

> . . . We are all entering this new world at the same moment in history . . . There is no way in which you can lean back on the past, or even on your contemporaries, and know what you want to teach . . . The children are our source of inspiration today in their fresh perception of a new world. It's no good for their elders to tell them what it used to be like. The young people say: "To hell with it. We don't want to hear what it was like." Because what it was like has almost nothing to do with the way things are. And this is what all of us have to understand. If we listen, later they will ask: "How was it?"

Indeed, as Jesse Reichek insists: "We teachers must risk the possibility of having our obsolescence and irrelevance demonstrated . . . If we acknowledge the value and the power of the students to awaken us to new issues, new values and new forms of action, let us make it possible for them to change us."

The emphasis on the individual as the primary source of values issues from the Existentialist thinking prevalent in our time. But it also stems from our conception of art today, from the only one that seems credible, art being defined as an aesthetic interaction between an individual and an object, idea, event; each individual literally creates in a process that is at its core personal and subjective what is art for him.

This attitude challenges a central assumption of the humanist tradition, that it is exemplified by the masterpiece, or a succession of masterpieces, whose values and standards have been determined through the ages by men of educated taste, and thus ought to shape our own judgments.

Art as subjective interaction also challenges the emphasis on objective analysis in the study and teaching of art history. To be sure, objective analysis is useful: to establish the date of a given work, the artist's name, the sequence of related objects, the intentions of the artist, the influences on him, the critical responses to his work, etc. As James C. Ackerman has written:

> The style of Objective Analysis . . . implies that one should attempt to examine one's material as objectively, as impersonally as possible in order to minimize the danger that one's own point of view might distort the interpretation of the material. To have a point of view at all is considered to be an unscientific position unless it can be demonstrated to be the result rather than the stimulus of investigation.

"Scientific" art historians have dominated the profession and have made suspect all attempts to deal with the more poetic and personal responses to art. Today, however, the values underlying objective analysis are being strongly criticized, and rightly so, on the grounds that this approach more often than not lapses into the fallacy of misplaced concreteness, as Louis Finkelstein has noted, cutting art to its own Procrustean bed. Furthermore, the past is not a closed body of facts to be dispassionately enumerated. It changes continually, depending on changing values, modes of examination, psychological quirks of scholars, etc.

Moreover, as Leo Steinberg has written:

> A refusal to suspend value judgments may be realistic in its own way. It reminds us that the objects of our inquiry depend for their sheer existence on admiration. Art is cherished, or it does not survive . . . To say it in other words, the record of past valuations is integrally part of art history, and that record is meaningless without present revaluation.

I do not propose that the existing art-historical curriculum be jettisoned, but that alternative or pluralistic approaches be considered. I should like to suggest two: one a new approach for teaching art history to future historians; the other, for teaching art history to art students.

Art history is usually taught with a predetermined chronology of Western art in mind and with predetermined notions concerning the significance of styles and artists that constitute a hierarchical order. There is an attempt to extend past tendencies and values into the present, but in practice teachers rarely get close to our own time. I propose that we begin from the vantage point of the present. Start the teaching of art history with the study of contemporary art and the conflicting issues deemed important now.

These issues can become the points of departure for reviewing the past, that is, allow the living present to give us our access to the vast realm of the past. In this way, we can determine what is of significance—alive or dormant at any moment—*in* the past, significant because it exposes how we arrived at the present and by contrast clarifies our awareness of both past and present. In turn, the past assumes a new importance, for it is imbued with meaning that it otherwise no longer seems to possess. To summarize, let the present regenerate those aspects of the past that illuminate and enrich the present.

My proposal stands chronology on its head, hopefully to get it back on its feet. To be sure, many teachers of art history will find it unnerving, even intolerable, to sacrifice linear continuity, for that provides art history with its securest means of coherence, but as I have suggested, the radical dislocation of past and present has called the relevance of habitual chronological arrangement into question. Instead, we can ground our approach on the needs and problems of today.

Let me hasten to say that aside from the loss of linear

continuity, my proposal is not so radical as it may seem. In fact, the study of contemporary art is being introduced in growing numbers of universities and colleges all over the country, witness the Institute of Fine Arts of New York University. Moreover, at the Washington Square College, students have the option of beginning their study of art with modern art. This first step having been taken, further steps shaping other aspects of the study of art history can easily follow, if we will only be open.

No aspect of art history need be disregarded; however, its priority in the teaching of art history at any given time would always be subjected to questions: what is it important to learn? what do we teach and when? Concomitantly, no teacher of art history need necessarily change his values. There must certainly be a place for the "science-minded" scholar who investigates the minutiae of the past. But those who aspire to more than the verification of what can be verified should no longer assume that they are possessed of certainties to which allegiance is automatically due, as one used to honor one's father.

Above all, I should like to stress that my proposal does not call for a relaxation in the rigor of research. It simply raises questions about what a student proposes to investigate. For example, given the widespread interest today in a Minimalist aesthetic, it would seem rewarding for students to study the history of Neoplasticism or the Bauhaus or Russian Constructivism, particularly when one considers that such studies may also illuminate, if only by contrast, our current problems concerning the rehabilitation of our cities, indeed of our whole society. It may be that too strong an emphasis on present aesthetic issues may distort the past, but such distortion is unavoidable in any case. Each generation invariably rewrites history.

If my proposal is viable, it then follows that the role of the art critic, including of course historians who are

critics, becomes central, for it is he who is most concerned
with contemporary art and its conflicting and competing
values. Indeed, it is his function to interrelate the multi-
plicity of contemporary styles and aesthetic theories and
to indicate what is most vital in the immediate present—
and why—at least as far as he is concerned.

Just as the student of art history might start with contemporary art as his point of departure, so might the art
student in his study of art history, even more so, for in
his own work he cannot help but be immersed in contemporary art. But in the case of the art student, I should
like to propose that his study of art history begin from
the vantage point of his own work.

For a number of years now, I have been trying to bring
the disciplines of art history and the studio close together
—indeed to break down any barriers that might exist
between the two. At this stage, I have arrived at the
following method, which I have used in several seminars.

I ask that each art student bring examples of his work
into the classroom—one or two students each session depending on the size of the class. The class as a whole
then discusses the problems that the work of each student
poses, its expressive content and formal means, its relations to contemporary styles and its antecedents in art
history, and its aesthetic quality and the justifications for
value judgments. In this process, the attempt is made to
characterize the unique artistic identity of a student's
work at that point in his career, clarifying the sense of
its identity by comparisons with related works past and
present.

The following week I come prepared with a lecture on
the art history, including the most recent developments
in current art, of a particular student's work and then
open up my formal presentation for class discussion, not
the least of which is criticism of my approach. As an
additional requirement, I ask each student to investigate

in depth an aspect of his own art history, and, when time permits, to present a paper to the class for further discussion. I must admit that I am often astounded by the quality of the students' research, their trenchant and often original insights into past and contemporary styles.

More and more, I consider myself a member of the classes that I teach, one who has his own thing to do—namely to attempt to present the entire range of my subject, if I can, indeed if I am allowed to, and to facilitate a student's own search for knowledge and values. I have found that I can generally cover the same material using the approach just described as I do when I lecture on art history.

What is lost is chronology—but this can be obtained from assigned textbooks and monographs. What is gained, I believe, is a sense of immediacy and relevance that can generate vitality; the enthusiastic responsiveness of students, their immersion in art-historical problems—in many cases, lovingly—and the provocation of fresh and exciting insights.

TEACHING THE RICH

Carol Duncan

. . . .

*Despite the claims by almost everybody asso-
ciated with educational establishments concerning the need for innovation and experimentation, there remains, in most American
classrooms, a great resistance to any kind of
authentic change. Rocking the boat is a peril-
ous act in most schools—from the elementary
to the college level. Teachers who attempt significant departures from prescribed norms,
such as curriculum or evaluation procedures,
risk dismissal. Elsewhere in this book Howard
Conant points out: "If art teachers . . . are
too creative, messy, radical, modern, or abstract, or cannot come up with an annual
spring art exhibit as 'nice' as those in neighboring schools, their contracts are not likely to be
renewed." In fact, many scholars, working
both within the field of art education as well
as other fields, have claimed that the mediocre
individual who performs according to the book
has a much better chance of remaining employed than does the real innovator.*

*In this essay Carol Duncan describes what
can happen to the teacher who recognizes the
hopelessness of an entrenched curriculum; and*

*she attempts to smoke out some of the reasons
that such curricula are staunchly defended by
even those teachers (and administrators) of
progressive and liberal inclinations.*

*The author questions the traditional role of
the art historian in the modern university and
relates it to recent developments in art and
society. Finally she concludes that: "So far . . .
challenges from artists, teachers, and students
have had little effect on the real, ongoing operations of cultural institutions." And she
notes that ". . . the arguments of those who
urge that aesthetic experience should leave the
museums and become an integral part of life
. . . offer as 'alternatives' to present conceptions of art what amounts to old wine in new
bottles. . . ."*

*Carol Duncan is an art scholar specializing
in eighteenth- and nineteenth-century French
art and culture. She was active in organizing
the New Art Association in 1970 and has
taught at several schools including Chicago
City College and the City College of New
York.*

. . . .

The importance given to the arts in prestigious, liberal
arts colleges—the expensive, "good" schools—has always
aroused the envy of artists and humanists in the larger
state schools. Indeed, small, elite colleges are often taken
as models for special or experimental programs in state
schools, and many public educators are committed to
making such "quality" education accessible to everyone.
A laudable goal, it would seem, but one that rests on a
rather shaky assumption: that the democratization of

elitist, liberal arts education is possible. Recent experiences that I had in a prestigious liberal arts college have led me to believe that the arts and the humanities as they are generally defined by colleges and other cultural institutions are largely resistant to democratization. For, the very concept of art that is fostered and preserved by the established art order is largely irrelevant to the life situations of all but a few. At the same time, culture-dispensing institutions have built-in ideological safeguards that effectively dissipate and discredit serious attempts even to question established conceptions. To illustrate:

In 1969, having just finished my doctorate in art history, I began teaching in a small, liberal arts college whose reputation for experimental education attracted the sons and daughters of the affluent and educated. Few and small classes, together with long office hours, promoted easy relations with students and an open course structure in which students increasingly determined the content of classroom discussions. These revolved around the meanings of specific works of art (from the eighteenth, nineteenth, and twentieth centuries) in relation to their changing societies, the situations of artists, the ideals of patrons, etc. Debate about the past frequently led us to parallel issues in the present. A recurrent theme was the place of art in present culture—its confinement to the hushed and hallowed galleries of museums where, removed from all historical context, it virtually requires from the viewer passive, purely "aesthetic" contemplation. Students also explored the production and promotion of such objects of autonomous aesthetic experience for today's art market and museum world as well as the general tendency of modern society to consign creative activity to the ambiguous position of something both very important (more meaningful than common experience and highly status-conferring) and not important at all (totally useless and irrelevant to "real," material values). Many of my students, disenchanted with the present dichotomy between high and low culture, began to speculate about a world in which the aesthetic dimension would permeate common as well as special life activities. What is meant by "creative freedom," my creatively inclined art and literature majors began to ask, if to exist professionally as an artist one must produce the kind of commodities or performances that society certifies as Art?

The issues that I had been discussing with my students became concrete and real for me personally when the college committee that does the hiring and firing decided not to renew my contract and justified its decision on ideological grounds. Both verbally and in writing, I was charged with "overemphasizing the social aspects of art history" at the expense of "art appreciation." I was also taken to task for my (really quite timid) version of the open-structured course and for criticizing the cult of individualism that is especially rampant on this campus. Although the ideology that prompted these charges is based in idealist tradition, the particular form in which I met it deserves attention, for versions of it thrive in liberal arts colleges and humanities departments everywhere. To understand its special tone and emphases, it is helpful to recall the social and intellectual climate of America a generation ago. For, it is no accident that the individuals who found my approach to art history so objectionable were mostly humanists in their forties. They represent what younger people today are referring to as the humanism of the 1950s, since the kind of thinking this term conveys was at its height in the academic world during the postwar decades when that age group went through college and university. Now tenured professors, they have come into the power positions in their institutions, at precisely the moment when their values are being vigorously challenged by a new generation that grew up in a different world.

In the 1950s, however, the élan of dissenting youth was all theirs. While most of their generation went to college for technical, commercial, or professional training, they read poetry, wrote novels, and cultivated a taste for art. What they sought, at their idealistic best, were alternatives to the single-minded materialism of America's booming, postwar business world. These were the holdouts, the people who chose elegant, semi-bohemian poverty over the 9-to-5 rat race. In their quest for intellectual scope, meaningful values, and the exercise of personal sensibilities, they were drawn into the humanities, that is, into college and university careers—almost the only careers in American society that could (and to some extent still do) offer a place for the kind of intellectual activity and cultured life-styles they sought. Especially in literature, art history, and musicology, they found realms rich in precisely those qualities of experience negated by the rest of culture, and it is not without reason that they defended the realm of art as something distinct from common experience. Common American experience meant "conformity," killing yourself with mindless work for bigger, tinnier cars, jerry-built tract houses, low TV culture, and tasteless Kool-Aid. In a postwar America whose unlimited appetite for material growth threatened everything not subject to unit-cost accounting, those committed to the cause of art could look at the big new science buildings on campus from their own cluttered little quarters with a certain sense of superiority.

In some ways, their thinking was the academic counterpart to that of the Abstract-Expressionist painters, who could find a place for personal expression only within the confines of those big canvases whose surfaces became arenas for inner experience, intuitive choice, and the "free," expressive gesture. So, many in this generation of academic humanists came to regard the freedom to exercise one's personal sensibilities and to choose artistic forms as the symbol and then the paradigm of all human liberty. For these refugees from a philistine society, art, literature, and the other humanities represented a sacred grove, a free zone whose boundaries had to be zealously defined and defended. Indeed, aggressive enemies lurked everywhere, not only in the hostile, materialist world without, but in the university itself—in sociology, for example, and in other so-called sciences that regarded man and his spiritual achievements as products of social forces.

To many humanists educated in those Cold War years, the issue of individual freedom as they knew it in their youth must seem to have come wholly alive again, with today's youthful left now acting the part of adversary. Thus put on the defensive, they often react as if the only alternative to their position is what they deem to be the Old Left's reduction of all cultural manifestation to a simple economic determinism. Even those who probably know better are apt to become uncomfortable when faced with any serious attempt to relate social contingencies to artistic choices. To draw again from my own experience: at lunch one day, I found myself next to a specialist in eighteenth-century English literature, and, with the intention of making conversation, began telling him about a book of essays by the British art historian Ellis K. Waterhouse. In this book (*Three Decades of British Art, 1740–1770* [Philadelphia: American Philosophical Society, 1965]), Waterhouse places the art of Joshua Reynolds in its social-historical setting, relating it to both the desire for status among eighteenth-century English artists and the ideals of the aristocracy. In the course of his book, he not only describes Reynolds as a prig, but argues that the pompous portraits he painted for his Tory patrons reinforced their smugness and arrogance; that same Tory arrogance that hastened the American Colonies toward the Declaration of Independence. All this quite upset my colleague, who turned out to be a Reynolds lover. Reynolds, he gave me to understand, was a Great Artist, author of the *Discourses,* and should be treated as such—no more, no less. He insisted on knowing whether or not *I* thought Reynolds a Great Artist. My answer, that he did some good things, did not satisfy him. This same fellow turned up on the committee that was reviewing my contract, and in my interview with them opened the Reynolds question again. "Is it not true," he asked, "that you teach Reynolds as a social climber?" I tried to explain the issue, but my goose was already cooked. Having once declared social contingencies of the past or the present to be substantive issues in the history of art, I had committed the inadmissible transgression. For true establishment humanists, art must be treated ultimately and categorically as Art, to be revered for its own aesthetic sake *exclusive* of all other meanings. During the same interview, another committee member (this time a musicologist) kept asking me if I did or did not teach my students "art appreciation," making it evidently clear that my primary job was to teach students to value art for its aesthetic pleasure alone and that to teach other meanings as well was to lessen the aesthetic value of an object.

From where they stood, I must have looked decidedly too "political" in a negative sense and was probably suspect of the most simplistic Old Leftism—judging art strictly on the basis of whether or not it directly addressed itself to the class struggle. From my point of view, however, *they* looked political in the broadest social sense: their demand that art be approached exclusively as an occasion for purified aesthetic experience not only wrenches from it a good part of its human import, but all the while it touts the spiritual sustenance of art, it insures its accessibility to only a small and privileged circle of consumers.

Indeed, the art historian's traditional role, in schools

not only of this kind but less prestigious places as well, is precisely to transmit this ideology of aesthetic elitism. In the big state schools, humanities teachers may claim to be democratizing elitism for the masses by "civilizing" their students with exposure to high art—at least when they are not lamenting how few of their students are able to grasp the pearls cast before them. The failure of this endeavor, amply evidenced in those laments, in effect reinforces the gulf between the cultured and the uncultured. In contrast, the claim that art, literature, and music are civilizing or socially beneficial agents finds its greatest traction in expensive liberal arts colleges where one is privileged to be educating the children of professors, collectors, and museum trustees—the future guardians of established culture and its institutions. Here, if anywhere, are the students whose backgrounds and future lives make relevant a classroom experience in which all art, past and present, is approached as if it were explicitly made to be looked at in the vacuum of the museum or acquired for one's own pleasure. Here, traditional, undergraduate art history finds its best audience as it presents the history of art as so many objects, bracketing and magnifying stylistic qualities, extolling the innate genius with which each great master solved a formal or iconographic problem, drawing an occasional parallel from philosophy or some other humanistic discipline, and extracting the World Views and Ideas that furnish the realm of abstract, universal truths—all the while avoiding or playing down the social matrix of art and turning the anti-art intentions of much twentieth-century art to aesthetic profit by treating them as "formal advances" to be appreciated for their own sakes.

Again, in the setting of the prestigious liberal arts college, the mutually supportive relationship between establishment humanism and the larger social order finds especially favorable ground. At the one in which I taught, for example, although it is now going coeducational, the curricula (largely the liberal and creative arts) and the educational philosophy (the development of individual self-expression) are superbly cut for the social roles so many of its alumnae have played: affluent matrons who collect and patronize the arts. In a recent statement, the college's president described the school's educational aims exactly in accordance with their life situations:

> In opposition to the idea that college experience must educate the student to be something, a something determined by the established order of the world, this college, in the spirit of the liberal arts, dedicates itself to educating the student simply to be.

This is accomplished, continued the president, when the student pursues such "enduring questions" as "What is man?" and "Who am I?" for, "only through the study of the great achievements of the human spirit—drama, poetry, philosophy—can these questions become part of a person's life." Now, the only people whom our social structure encourages "simply to be"—in a cultured, liberal arts way, that is—are wealthy, leisured women, probably America's major consumers (but not producers) of high culture. Establishment humanism and its related cult of individualism give both substance and ideological justification to this activity. While extolling the value of individual creativity, it certifies creative activity only in the form of objects or acts produced for the contained spheres of the art world, implicitly justifying the absence of aesthetic values in so-called common experience. And while proclaiming the meanings of these objects and acts to be universal and theoretically available to all men, it turns its back on the fact that the physical and mental lives of most people are *socially* organized so that no matter how many free days the museums offer, they have neither the interest and training nor the social and geographical proximity with which to benefit from these supremely humanizing products. [1] Thus establishment humanism protects and perpetuates the value of art in forms that insure its existence as a subculture, conserving both its authentic spiritual rewards and its real social prestige for the rich and those who serve them.

Since the late 1960s, challenges to the established art order and its ideology have been increasing, touching every sector of the institutionalized art world. They have come from artists intent on changing their normal relationships to museums and the art market and from scholars, critics, and teachers who are no longer content to transmit established values and modes of judgment unexamined. Other, more pervasive forces are also at work in discrediting the prestige of the art world. Most important perhaps is the increasing suspicion with which young people regard all established institutions and ideologies. The values of self-expression and self-knowledge—the refusal to join the 9-to-5 crowd—still attract the young, and especially the affluent young. However, the attraction is not the same as it was in the 1950s when such values could provide sufficient life goals to a dissenting, antimaterialist youth. In the 1970s the appeal of the

[1] Teachers in public colleges may protest that many of their students demonstrate high interest and capacity in art appreciation in spite of nonsupportive family backgrounds. I am sure they do. But what happens to them after they leave college and enter their working lives? Unless they join up with the intellectual establishment and thus escape the work world—and this requires exceptional skills and mobility—most of them will have neither the opportunities nor the interest to involve themselves with art on a continuing basis. It does not necessarily follow that they are any the poorer for being deprived of high culture *as our institutions define it.* (Conversely, I am not arguing that "low" or mass culture is therefore good art.) My point here is that institutions that claim to disseminate high culture to the masses do not fulfill their claims (see Linda Nochlin, "Museums and Radicals: A History of Emergencies," *Art in America* [July–August, 1971], pp. 26–39) .

academic humanities must compete with the conviction that one has as much or more to gain personally in a changed social order and in the qualitatively different human relationships such change would bring. Whatever real effects the various youth movements might have on American society, they have at least begun to shatter the illusion that the ivory tower exists removed from the bad things in society, preserving and perpetuating only the good.

So far, however, challenges from artists, teachers, and students have had little effect on the real, ongoing operations of cultural institutions, where establishment humanism remains a viable ideology. Those protesting the irrelevance of high culture constitute but a fraction—and a powerless one—of an already small minority (the art world), and their voices hardly carry beyond the select readership of art pages and special magazines. At the same time, within institutions, issues are rarely discussed at their deepest levels; the concerned professors, museum directors, and artists addressing themselves to the "crisis," i.e., the cultural blight in which most people live, frequently end by perpetuating the very conceptions of art and artists they began by contesting. Such are the arguments of those who urge that aesthetic experience should leave the museums and become an integral part of life but who offer as "alternatives" to present conceptions of art what amount to old wine in new bottles: anti-object art that still commands a mode of experience sealed off from other values and life activities and that remains incomprehensible to those whose life situations deny them the difficult intellectual preparation it demands. Such also are the arguments of educators that we should democratize high culture by disseminating it more vigorously to the "culturally deprived"—a Raphael in every home as it were. But, no amount of art education will be effective so long as other aspects of existence remain untouched. Aesthetic consciousness cannot simply be sprinkled over a social reality that is virtually organized to repel it in the minds of all but a few. Until there are essential and substantive changes in that reality, aesthetic values will remain the monopoly of those initiated into the subculture of Art.

Ernesto J. Ruíz de la Mata

THE ART CRITIC AS A PEDAGOGUE

Ernesto J. Ruíz de la Mata

· · · · · · · · · · · · · · · · · · · ·

*Because the art critic "lacks the security" that
the historian has come to depend upon, he is
a gambler, and sometimes a loser. Yet he is
also a teacher—sometimes in fact, and always
in spirit.*

*De la Mata finds the provincial critic suffer-
ing abuses not normally encountered by the
big-city critic, although many critics residing
in and working out of the art centers would
probably point out other hazards endemic to
their position.*

*This essay makes no attempt to define and
clarify the role of the critic—it merely points
out the difficulties faced by critics today. In
his conclusion, de la Mata states that "the
ideal situation of an excellent artist, a receptive public, an intelligent editor, and a responsible art critic do not always coincide."
Amen.*

De la Mata is art critic for the San Juan
Star *in San Juan, Puerto Rico. He is program
director for the American Section of the International Association of Art Critics.*

· · · · · · · · · · · · · · · · · · · ·

"To be just, that is to say, to justify its existence, criticism should be partial, passionate and political, that is to say, written from an exclusive point of view, but a point of view that opens up the widest horizons."—BAUDELAIRE

The idea of an art critic as a "pedagogue" may be a rather complex phenomenon, since at the university level the critic may very well be a professor, and therefore a "teacher."

There is a distinction that is often made in the United States between the "art historian," the "art critic," and the "art educator."

This, I daresay, only makes sense within a country whose educational structure is divided in such a specialized manner that the art educator is more concerned with the training of a student in the various techniques of art, teaching him "art appreciation" or its equivalent, and simultaneously feeding him pedagogical theories that will help him convey that very same training he has been under to his future pupils. A vicious circle indeed!

Yet, the hiatus between an art historian and an art critic is not a real one. The main difference consists in how the game is played by either of them.

When an art historian uses his sources and methods of research in a scientific manner to arrive at certain conclusions that are imaginative, creative, and that should throw new light upon an epoch, an artist, or a more specialized theme within the organizational structure of a paper, an essay, or a book, he is not too far away from an art critic.

The art critic uses the same mechanisms of investigation with similar intentions. The difference consists in that he has to do mainly with contemporary phenomena. Research is thus limited in scope, but not necessarily limited in depth.

The art critic lacks the security that depends upon previous observations, criticisms, treatises, and theses, which are the kind of manured graze upon which the art historian feeds himself.

The art critic gambles . . . And he always places his chips on a given number on the roulette wheel. Naturally, he needs to have sufficient knowledge and a thorough training with which to back up his bet, and allow him to keep on with the game. It is permissible to lose once in a while, but never too much and not too often. There is nothing more pathetic than a losing critic. Perhaps this does not come to the mind of everyone, because once he has lost on too many occasions he seems magically to vanish into a kind of limbo.

Meanwhile, the art historian may remain as an unperturbed and aloof onlooker seeing the present from his lofty Olympian height.

An analogy can be established with the case of a person who suffers from nearsightedness—indeed, myopia should be established as a prerequisite for anyone who wishes to take up a career in art criticism or art history.

Myopia physically allows the individual to take off his corrective eyeglasses and get up as near as possible to a painting or a sculpture for a close-up view of details that would make someone with normal vision dizzy, or step back gradually, at different intervals, so as to see the diverse color zones or areas without the intrusion of shape as a defined form. The latter can be done once he has put on his spectacles again.

In this same dialectical manner one can think of intuition and the intuitive approach toward the work of art as equivalent to proximity to the painting without spectacles.

But once this sort of initial rapport is achieved, a different perspective is indispensable.

It is then that the "eyeglasses," which are constituted by a synchronous and gradual training of the eye and mind, by a continuous process of accumulation and sifting of knowledge, will provide the balance for the correct appreciation and evaluation of the work of art.

Once that is accomplished, then the art critic's ideas are put down in a more or less elegant manner, in a verbiage that in the Southern European fashion depends much more upon literary style and "good taste" than factual knowledge, or in the German phenomenological and positivistic tradition into a drab, dry, barren prose which, nonetheless, gives the interested reader a true and sharp insight into the core of the art object.

If you do not know a word about art education as such; if you do not give a damn about carrying out the type of work that more properly appertains to the vocational rehabilitator or the social worker; then, in an always responsible manner and backed up by your knowledge, training, and good taste, your opinions might serve as a guideline to lead others to see into the work of art, to grasp in the group of works that an artist is exhibiting what should be seen in them and to gloss over not only those shows that are not worthy of their time and will waste away their vision in a pollution of lines, colors, shapes, and surfaces, but save it up for other more meritorious occasions.

As such, then, there is no great difference between the art critic and the film critic. The only possible difference would be whether the public does not want to benefit from the element of suspense and surprise and is not worried about the "story," but about the manner in which it is told. Yet, there are many movie fans who prefer to see the film first and read the criticism afterward. There are others who save up their time and money by relying upon the judgment of those critics whom they respect, thereby making it possible to augment not only their enjoyment but their culture as well through a more discriminate application of their time.

Thus, the art critic also might very well carry on a responsible function within the society.

But then, it all depends upon what kind of a "society" the art critic is addressing himself to. Is it a parochial society? If it is a society in which being an "artist" and flaunting that label is enough to gain the respect of his fellow citizens and command their admiration, then that becomes the plight of the art critic!

In New York, Boston, or Los Angeles a critic can lash out as viciously as he wishes if that violence comes from a true conviction of what he dislikes and as long as he extolls the virtues of those works that appeal to his sensibility without causing a great tremor or disruption within the society itself.

In the case of provincial communities that are more accustomed to the dithyrambic eulogies of "Atheneum" orations or to the type of ecstatic journalistic criticism that fits more with the Society Page of the newspaper rather than in a column dedicated to the arts the critic is doomed.

When the means of conveying his message is the Sunday Supplement of the local newspaper the readers often, through their lack of sophistication, turn against the art critic if they are friends of such and such an artist, his pupils, collectors, or the owners and associates of the gallery that represents him, and therefore resent the unfavorable comments made about the show.

Unfortunately, the ideal situation of an excellent artist, a receptive public, an intelligent editor, and a responsible art critic do not always coincide.

Notwithstanding, we must remember that sometimes it might be the art critic who is to be blamed for not taking off his spectacles if he is near enough to a painting to be able to see it and for putting them back on again when he is far enough away to be able to "get the total picture."

. . . .

ART EDUCATION:
CRITICISMS

Howard Conant

SEASON OF DECLINE

Howard Conant

. . . .

Howard Conant, professor and Chairman of the Department of Art Education at New York University, takes a dim view of what passes for art education in most schools today. He feels that much of it is often ". . . so poor in quality that it does more harm than good" and he goes on to note "The branch of learning that only euphemistically can be called art education propagates rather than counteracts cultural mediocrity. It misleads and confuses, rather than educates and clarifies."

Conant envisions a kind of art education that counteracts ". . . technology, mass media, and the very 'business' of art itself," which, he feels, ". . . pose[s] critical threats to the survival of essential humanistic concerns." More specifically, he writes here that "The kind of art education I have in mind . . . has practically nothing to do with the meaningless piddling around with art materials and superficial art appreciation that typifies most present-day programs. . . ."

In a characteristically outspoken manner, Conant points out that ". . . the moment art became an element of formal education and

*teaching became the responsibility of peda-
gogues rather than artists, art as such practically vanished from the educational scene."*

*Ultimately we are faced with questions of
judgment and quality. Conant claims: "Quite
simply, there are no established, tangible, universal criteria of incremental progress or excellence in the arts."*

*In this essay Conant raps educators, certifi-
cation and licensing bureaus, administrators,
and school board members. His job, besides
running the Art Education Department at
N.Y.U., is head of the Division of Creative
Arts. He is author of* Art Education *(New
York: Center for Applied Research in Education, 1964) and has written many articles.*

. . . .

"We come from a world where we have known incredible
standards of excellence, and we dimly remember beauties
which we have not seized again."—THORNTON WILDER

". . . for it would be rash to assume that the season of
decline is unfavorable in every respect. . . . What remains
are hidden deposits . . . where perchance the more precious
crystals grow."—ORTEGA Y GASSET

One of the few generally agreed upon characteristics of
art is that the harder you consciously try to create it, the
less likely you are to succeed. Perhaps art's poorest relative, art education, has earned its reputation for inferi-
ority and has failed to do what it presumably set out to
do because it did what it did too consciously. Trying too
consciously to teach art (rather than, say, painting or
sculpture) is probably just as poor an idea as consciously
setting out to create art (rather than a painting or a piece

of sculpture), or, poorer still, setting out to create a major work of art.

But whatever the causal factors may be, it is fairly common knowledge that what passes for art education in most elementary and secondary schools and recreation programs, and in many colleges and professional art schools is often so poor in quality that it does more harm than good. The branch of learning that only euphemistically can be called *art* education propagates rather than counteracts cultural mediocrity. It misleads and confuses, rather than educates and clarifies. It offers shortcuts to art that turn out to be permanent detours, teaches gimmicks that impede the development of self-evolved techniques, and provides meaningless recipes for instant aesthetics. It has so little to do with art, and is, in fact, so downright bad, that it should probably be suspended until teams of top professional, educationally enlightened, and socially concerned artists, critics, historians, philosophers, sociologists, psychologists, and leaders of cultural affairs in government and philanthropic foundations could be brought together to plan a culturally and educationally viable program of total, continuing education in the visual arts.

As it stands today, art education is basically meaningless, culturally purposeless, and artistically ludicrous. It retards rather than enhances artistic expression and critical awareness. Indeed, there is hardly a professional artist, critic, historian, or artistically enlightened layman who will say that he can do what he can do, or knows what he knows, *because* of his art education rather than in spite of it.

What is to be done? Can the teaching of art, like the teaching of science and mathematics, be completely revamped, rejuvenated, and made relevant to basic human interests and needs? Or was Auguste Herbin right when

Warrior jar, earthenware, Colima style of West Mexico, 100
B.C.–A.D. 250. Jay C. Leff Collection.

he said that "the teaching of art is ill-fated and completely useless"? Should art education not simply be
abolished, and the time, money, and effort thus saved be
put to better use?

My personal reaction is that Herbin, like a considerable number of others who share his pessimism, was
wrong. Art education is not ill-fated: it has simply been
misguided and mishandled, and needs to be set straight.
Art education is not useless: what has passed for art education is, indeed, useless; but the kind of art education
proposed here can be shown to be absolutely essential
to our lives. If we really want to save ourselves from the
quicksand of cultural mediocrity in which we are already
up to our elbows, we had better be quick and able in
bringing about radical changes in art-educational practices.

The kind of art education I envision is crucially important to all persons and all societies, particularly at
this point in time when technology, mass media, and the
very "business" of art itself pose critical threats to the
survival of essential humanistic concerns. The kind of
art education I envision needs first to be brought to the
minimum level of excellence that is essential to its proper
functioning as a positive, constructive force in the kind
of society to which Thornton Wilder referred as having
had "incredible standards of excellence" in the arts. The
kind of art education I envision can not only restore to
our lives the "dimly remembered beauties" of past civilizations, but can also help us create and cultivate new,
fresh beauties in contemporary life as well.

The kind of art education I have in mind, however,
has practically nothing to do with the meaningless piddling around with art materials and superficial art appreciation that typifies most present-day programs. But in
order to effect proper reforms, we need to know why art
education is in the poor condition it is in today. We need

to know exactly where and how our predecessors as well as we ourselves have erred so that we do not needlessly replicate mistakes. We also need to know how, on occasion, our predecessors did begin to produce fruitful art-educational results, and why they became sidetracked.

Our very earliest art-educational predecessors did very well indeed—without, it should be noted, the aid of formally educated teachers. The caveman's form of art education can only have been what we know as the master/apprentice system. Of course, we don't know exactly how "liberal arts" learning was handled by early man, but it seems abundantly clear that his cave drawings were "understood" and treated with considerable respect by many of his fellowmen who saw or were told about them. The fact is clear, however, that the master/apprentice system, augmented by word of mouth or other means of aesthetic value dissemination, not only worked but worked exceedingly well. History is full of examples of art masterworks and periods of cultural enlightenment that can be attributed to this art-educational system.

Art education as a school subject was not introduced until the nineteenth century, and it was precisely here that the troubles with which we are presently faced really started. Whatever drawbacks to creative expression and art connoisseurship may have been inherent in the master/apprentice system—and judging from the quality of works produced from the prehistoric era through the late Renaissance, and the psychological and sociological effects these works must have had upon persons who experienced them, they were certainly minimal—the integrity of art as such was unimpaired.

But the moment art became an element of formal education and teaching became the responsibility of pedagogues rather than artists, art as such practically vanished from the educational scene. Art and artists were relegated to museums, churches, the homes of the wealthy, and ateliers. Elementary and secondary schools and colleges were, and for the most part still are, artistically barren institutions, which in both appearance and function detract from rather than contribute to cultural concerns.

The "art" that was, and still is, taught in schools and colleges can best be described as busywork. It had, and still has, practically nothing to do with either the creation or study of genuine art. The "art" that was introduced as a school subject in the early 1800s was a kind of soft-edged mechanical drawing. Though incredibly slavish, it was called "freehand drawing." After a few really uptight decades of rendering and shading bottles and plaster casts, an equally constricting activity called "art appreciation" was introduced, probably because some fumbling theorists thought there had been too much "doing" and not enough "thinking" and "feeling." But no sooner had the little ladies (and men) who taught "art" developed some really effective ways of imposing their own truly academic taste upon their pupils than art-educational theorists of a different persuasion (themselves, no doubt, largely persuaded by burgeoning sales of their own textbooks) quickly gained favor, and "expression" was back in the buggy of what was regarded as art-educational progress. This time it may have been clay modeling (of inane subjects) rather than pencil sketching that gained favor. But these slight alterations in educational emphasis were more symptoms of art teachers' ambivalence than of their genuine persuasion.

The pendular behavior of art educators continued. In the early decades of the twentieth century it was "picture study" (another name for art appreciation) and school trips to art museums (featuring museum cafeterias and souvenir shops) that gained favor (having no relation at all, quite naturally, to the exciting avant-garde art styles that were sweeping Europe and were being shown to and by the cognoscenti at Steiglitz' Gallery 291, the Armory Show of 1913, etc.). Then it was on again (actually back) in the 1930s and 1940s to an "invention" of the Progressive Education movement called "creativity" (seldom art, but always "do what you please," whether you wanted to or not). Following this, in the 1950s, came "sequentially structured studies" of works of art (actually reproductions) of supposedly increasing profundity. Art-educational theorists of the 1960s cooked up a grandly broad, cognitively-based "construct" called "aesthetic education" and claimed to have found at last the long-sought route to the "affective domain" of human behavior.

The curriculum area, which, as we have shown, can only gratuitously be called art education, has been plagued with goal-orientation amibvalence and theoretical gobbledygook during the entire century-plus period of its existence. Art teachers have vacillated irresponsibly from one philosophic emphasis to' another, never pursuing a particular objective long enough to reach a stage of possible fruition. Had even the most rigidly academic or, conversely, the most creative of these objectives been followed through to a logical conclusion, art education might have found its way.

How welcome indeed, and how potentially fruitful, might have been an Ingres-like focus upon the discipline of representational drawing, a Hofmannesque exploration of explosive creativity in painting, or a Cornellian exploration of the mystique of surrealist constructions. And how deeply rewarding might have been truly concentrated studies of primordial imagery in abstract painting, penetrating studies of archetypal form preferences as possible bases of art-style choice, or detailed investigations of physiological responses to various types of iconography.

The lack of goal orientation stick-to-it-iveness on the part of teachers is, however, only one of several causal factors that have led to the present condition of art-educational ineffectuality.

Almost without exception, for example, professional organizations in the field of art education have pacified and entertained, rather than stimulated and educated, their members. The meetings and publications of these organizations have been anything but scholarly in nature, and have, in fact, occasionally become ludicrous ("cowgirls" at the 1971 National Art Education Association in Dallas sang "Ya gotta have art" and handed out lapel pins emblazoned with the same insipid slogan). The professionally respectable College Art Association treats art educators like country cousins; and the Institute for the Study of Art in Education, a professional organization commendably dedicated to scholarly and artistically significant pursuits, has attracted to membership only about one hundred of the probable ten or fifteen thousand teachers in the field of art education.

With pitifully few exceptions (Paul Klee, László Moholy-Nagy, Walter Gropius, Kenneth Clark, etc.), leading practitioners and scholars in the arts have failed to involve themselves directly with educational matters, and even these few have almost entirely limited their interests and activities to higher and professional education or, as in the case of Lord Clark, to television. Practically none of them has taught in or has become directly involved with art education programs in elementary or secondary schools, and only those artists and scholars who have earned doctorates are treated as other than second-class citizens in many colleges and universities. On rare occasions, they are asked to speak at art education meetings or write for art education journals, but the poor reception usually accorded such ventures more often than not causes them to say "never again."

Following the lead (in this case, *not* desirable) of either

established conservative or well-known avant-garde scholars and practitioners in the arts (both groups are treated
with unwarranted overrespect), art educators have, depending on their pathetically blind allegiance to either
the more conservative or more liberal of these two per-
suasions, either excluded architecture, environmental design, film, videotape, the interdisciplinary arts, and various commercial art forms from their range of interest in
what they consider to be the arts, or they have become
ludicrously McLuhanesque and have thrown out everything but the newest electronic media. The conservative
group is quixotically trying to keep alive the myth of the
"fine arts" of painting and sculpture, and as a result both
they and the scholars and practitioners they emulate are
not only out of touch with most students' primary interests—they are really out of touch with the very times in
which they live! The avant-garde sympathizers, on the
other hand, are almost too closely in touch with students'
current and often transitory interests, frequently emulate
their patterns of speech, dress, and behavior, and offer
few alternatives to the "air-conditioned nightmare" of a
technologized culture that Herbert Read, George Orwell,
Aldous Huxley, and Stanley Kubrick have so frighten-
ingly and persuasively portrayed. What is needed, of
course, is a balanced art-educational program in which
all major historic and contemporary art forms are studied
in the fullest-possible cultural context, augmented by
personal creative work in media pertinent to each period,
style, and medium.

To delineate the particulars of art-educational ineptitude further may be like beating a dead horse; yet as
Ortega y Gasset has reassuringly explained, "it would
be rash to assume that the season of decline is unfavorable in every respect."

A major and continuing problem of art education has
been the (seeming) need to fit it and other presumably

atypical school subjects like music, drama, and dance, into conventional school patterns of scheduling, deportment, incremental development, and evaluation. We are probably wrong in thinking that programs of study in *any* curriculum area (mathematics, for example) can function effectively within the conventional school schedule of fifty-minute class periods, five days a week, forty weeks per year. We may be wrong in thinking that students develop incrementally from what are thought to be elementary to advanced stages of understanding in subjects such as mathematics and physical science. And we may be wrong in thinking that there are established norms that can be used in evaluating concept development in subjects such as biology and sociology.

But we are certainly not wrong in thinking that art cannot effectively be "turned on" at 8:35 A.M. each Monday, Wednesday, and Friday, and then be "turned off" fifty minutes later; neither are we wrong in thinking that even with the most "avant-garde," flexible, or "open-school" scheduling during the week can genuine art interests and motivations be suspended during after-school and evening hours, weekends, and school vacations. Artists and scholars do indeed work with a degree of regularity, but they are motivated to do so by a kind of inspiration and involvement that has nothing to do with identical work schedules.

We are certainly not wrong in thinking that the life-style and behavioral characteristics of artists and scholars differ markedly from those that might be said to typify the population of most school environments. More often than not, persons involved in the process of creation and scholarship in art prefer to work alone, rather than in groups; and although some of them may enjoy hearing music, conversation, or even traffic noises while they work, others require comparative quiet. Some artists require a studio atmosphere and a personal dress style of almost antiseptic neatness, whereas others find a completely relaxed, even messy work situation most conducive to their creative work, and they dress accordingly.

Lastly, we are certainly not wrong in thinking that the educational notions of incremental development and evaluation that are currently popular in several academic disciplines are relatively inapplicable to the arts. In the cases of art history and criticism, for example, abstract art is not *better* or *more advanced* than, say, surrealist art: it is merely *different*. "High Renaissance" art is not *better* or *more advanced* than that of the "Early Renaissance": it was merely produced later chronologically. Prehistoric or primitive art is as sophisticated aesthetically as Classical or Impressionist art. In terms of art media and processes (which are peculiarly favorite concerns of art teachers and may thus be providing us with a psychological clue to their trouble that has not yet been investigated), there is no hierarchy of elementary-through-advanced media and techniques. Contrary to the seemingly benevolent doctrines of nearly all art education textbooks, crayon drawing is not simpler or more rudimentary than oil painting, neither is chalk drawing more appropriate for children (or, say, "beginning artists") than etching or wood carving. A large, hand-painted landscape in oils by Monet is not necessarily *better* than a ten by fourteen inch, mass-produced photo silk-screen print by Warhol; neither is one more appropriate than another as a subject for study by children at a particular age level or by art scholars. Artists do not necessarily get *better* as they get older, neither are the works upon which they spend the most time or effort or for which they do the most research or for which they receive the highest price necessarily their *best*. By the same token, the creative works produced by children in the sixth grade are not necessarily *better* than those produced by first graders. A work of art created by a child at the end of the

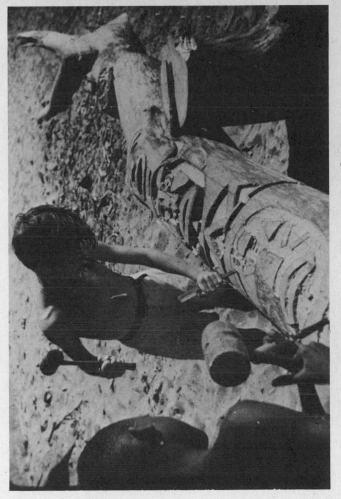

Ten-year-old boys carving totem pole..

academic year is not necessarily *better* aesthetically than one he produced at the beginning of the year; it is only "another work," which may or may not be better, and may or may not indicate that he has progressed, regressed, or remained stable. A given work of art created by a particular child (or by a particular professional artist) may elicit praise from one art teacher (or art critic) and an unfavorable response from another. Quite simply, there are no established, tangible, universal criteria of incremental progress or excellence in the arts. On the other hand—and contradiction *is* an accepted norm in the arts—there *are* certain works of art that elicit fairly universal (though differently based and stated) praise from a broad segment of the artistic community; but the reasons given by various individuals within such a group for praising particular works of art are so varied that an "outsider" would consider such seeming accord invalid.

On the surface, it would seem that elementary and secondary school art teachers are the chief cultural culprits, but they are only the most visible members of what really amounts to a frightfully effective anticultural coalition that is comprised, albeit unwittingly, of the faculties of college art-teacher-education departments, art-teacher-certification bureaus, teachers of all subjects at all educational levels, parents of children from preschool through college age, school administrators, laymen, and the purveyors of inartistry in environmental design, architecture, interior design, furnishings, advertising, packaging, industrial design, and the mass media.

The purveyors of inartistry are, of course, not at all naïve or unwitting, and hence qualify as "professional" members of the anticultural coalition. It is in the best interests of modern economics (i.e., television and magazine ads) to propagate, they claim, designs that range from the ever-popular mediocre to the increasingly fash-

TENSE, NERVOUS HEADACHES

Acts Instantly to Give More Complete Pain Relief

How Tension Headaches Start

1.

Tension builds up in neck and scalp muscles . . .

ANACIN relaxes tension,

ionable tawdry. Also worthy of mention in any listing of the components of blame for art-educational ineffectuality are the institutions that prepare art teachers, the state and municipal education departments that certify or license them, and the boards of education and administrators to whom teachers are professionally responsible.

More often than not, art teachers teach as they have been taught; hence, it will come as no surprise to learn that their ineptitude is nothing more than a reflection of a malaise inherited from the college or university art education departments in which they were prepared. As art teachers gain experience, advanced degrees, and something of a reputation for effectively propagating one form or another of art-educational dogma, they are invited to return to art-teacher-education institutions as faculty members, thus completing another arc in the vicious circle of art-educational ineptitude.

State and city art teacher certification and licensing bureaus, often staffed with advanced-degree-holding, former teachers of art, are seldom more than rubber-stamp agencies that ceremoniously raise and lower, according to educational fashion, the art-educational hemlines of minimum and maximum requirements for assorted studio, methods, and art history courses.

The school board members and administrators to whom art teachers are professionally responsible are, of course, made up in the best "democratic" fashion of persons without "vested interests" in art or, for that matter, without deep and abiding interests in anything except the "neatness, frugality, cleanliness, and punctuality" syndrome to which D. H. Lawrence in his famous *Studies in Classic American Literature* (1923) diatribe on "the establishment" took more sustained and precise exception. Artistically and aesthetically, school administrators and board members are usually laymen in the plainest sense of the term. They quite naturally praise, rather than criticize, the production of superficial art projects and the acquisition of shallow aesthetic concepts, which to them seem "pretty," "useful," "interesting," or "sensible." If art teachers in the schools run by such administrators and board members are too creative, messy, radical, modern, or abstract, or cannot come up with an annual spring art exhibit as "nice" as those in neighboring schools, their contracts are not likely to be renewed.

The frequent failure of school board members and administrators to make worthwhile and adequate learning-resource materials available to art teachers and their pupils is another major cause of art-educational ineffectuality. Art teachers are literally expected to teach "off the tops of their heads" when it comes to resource materials in art. Most of them, sad to say, *expect* to do this, having been trained to get along on a shoestring when it comes to school budgets. But the fact of the matter is that even the most enlightened, best-educated, and quick-witted art teacher is faced with almost insurmountable obstacles to achievement if he wishes to make adequately sustained and meaningful use of slides, reproductions, films, reference books, art periodicals, and particularly original works of art in his instructional program. A thoughtfully programmed, continuing series of field trips to museums, design centers, artists' studios, and architectural sites within, say, a hundred-mile radius of the school is out of the question. And the two most important of all learning-resource materials in the arts, original works of art and artists themselves, are almost completely unheard of in elementary and secondary schools, except in the rarest of instances where a foundation or government grant brings "artists-in-residence" or a traveling exhibition to a few schools selected on an experimental, usually one-time, and hence almost meaningless basis. The prevailing situation in art education is roughly analogous to what it would be like to teach literature without being able to use unabridged literary works and without being able to hire writers or critics as teachers or not even being able to bring them in as part-time teachers or occasional speakers (which again, sadly, is usually the case).

The fact that elementary school language arts and secondary school English teachers are at least generally able to use the finest, original, uncut, unwatered-down novels, poems, plays, and essays goes a long way toward accounting for the comparatively high level of verbal literacy among high-school graduates. But very few of these same students, unfortunately, have developed *visual* literacy, and like their parents, and their parents' parents before them, they have to admit that they "can't draw a straight line" and that they "don't know much about art but they know what they like." The aforementioned cliché responses are in themselves fairly good evidence of visual illiteracy, since straight-line-drawing ability has little to do with significance in art expression and, paradoxically, knowing what one likes *does* have a great deal to do with understanding art!

The blame for educational ineffectuality, then, obviously should not be limited to art teachers. Indeed, one might ask, what could even the most enlightened and able art teachers do even to stem, let alone counteract, the plethora of inartistry with which their pupils are enveloped during nearly every waking hour? In the context of the approximately sixteen nonsleeping hours per day or one hundred twelve hours per week that most pupils spend in environments of harshly unaesthetic banality, some three hours per day or twenty-one hours per week of which are absorbed with heinously effective inartistry at the receiving end of assorted television transmissions, what could one expect from even the most Herculean efforts on the part of an art teacher? What possible effect could, let us generously say, even several hours per week of the most enlightened and effective art teaching have upon pupils who live in such overwhelmingly inartistic environments?

The rather surprising answer to the questions posed by the aforementioned descriptions of art-educational ineffectuality and anticultural social conditions is, quite simply, that a few hours per week of enlightened and effective art teaching *can* have a resoundingly positive effect upon both pupils and the overall cultural conditions of their society. To a great extent this is due to the little-recognized fact that elementary and secondary school children highly respect and can be deeply and lastingly influenced by a really well-informed and able teacher. Children really do not believe in the sensationalistic, often dishonest hucksterism that dominates the mass media (though without the influence of a good art teacher, they will eventually be conditioned into believing in it); and they strongly disapprove of much of the ugliness in their environment. They literally thirst for integrity and for demonstrations of genuine ability in the persons who serve as their teachers. For this reason, among others, the idea of employing the finest-possible practicing, professional artists, art critics, and art historians as teachers of art on a part- or full-time basis in elementary and secondary schools makes excellent sense. In spite of the obvious and serious limitations of current educational conditions, such as inflexible scheduling and inadequate learning-resource materials, an enormous first step toward art-educational reform and cultural regeneration can be taken at once by means of: first, persuading artists, critics, and historians of the cultural essentiality of their services to elementary and secondary schools and colleges; and second, persuading school boards, administrators, and certification bureaus to recruit and employ teachers in these categories and to accept their professional accomplishments in lieu of formal training and advanced degrees.

It is, of course, to be expected that some professional artists, art critics, and art historians will not work out as well as might be desired in a given school situation, and that adjustments will have to be made or replacements sought. But given wide enough application and a reasonable amount of time, the employment of professionals in the arts in elementary and secondary schools and colleges is bound to pay educational as well as cultural dividends. Once initiated, the practice of employing professionals in the arts as teachers at all educational levels has certain built-in guarantees of success. As these professionals learn of the congeniality and stimulation of modern school environments, the eagerness, ability, sincerity, and affection of pupils, not to mention the salaries that teachers are paid, which compare more than favorably with the limited earnings of most artists, many art critics, and some art historians, schools will be deluged with applications from which they can select the persons best qualified as artist-teachers.

It's about time we put the "art" back into art education. Works of art, the artists who produce them, and the critics and historians who study, analyze, and interpret them are the primary components of the entity we know as "art." Works of art, in themselves, are difficult and often very expensive to acquire, and their use in educational institutions entails complicated and also costly problems of security and display. Artists, critics, and historians are, however, readily available, greater in number than ever before in history, often in need of an income to support their artistic productivity, and can be employed to fill staff vacancies at no net increase in instructional budgets. On at least an experimental, limited basis, we should thus initiate a long overdue reform in art education by bringing professionals in the arts into the very nerve center of cultural regeneration, which the finest programs of education in the arts represent. By this means, we might be able to transform the season of decline into an era of artistic and aesthetic excellence.

Allen Leepa

ART AND SELF:
THE MORPHOLOGY OF TEACHING ART

Allen Leepa

. . . .

Allen Leepa claims that a major change of our time that is reflected in the behavior of man is a ". . . shift in emphasis from external to internal authority." In the area of art teaching he declares that "important creativity comes from the student's own self-motivated inspirations" and not necessarily from the assignments and directions coming from the teacher that arise from clearly defined and specific concepts and proposals.

In this article Leepa explains why the student must be urged to explore his own interests and ". . . those feelings, ideas, and sensations that to him are most meaningful." The instructor's ideas and attitudes should not be prescribed; if so the result will be twofold— educational crises in a democratic society and identity confusion.

What this all boils down to is that the shift in art teaching from academic realism to creative self-expression has not resulted in sufficient clarification of how a student "discovers his own path in art." Indeed, that's the question. In a way we're back where we started.

Allen Leepa teaches at Michigan State University and is author of The Challenge of Modern Art *(Cranbury, N.J.: A. S. Barnes & Co., 1961). He is working on another book dealing with the problems and education of the painter today, from which this article is excerpted.*

. . . .

Man is under great pressure to define himself—territorially, by physical space; socially, by status; emotionally, by dependence and independence; psychologically, by goals and roles. In recent years, he has become less dependent on external authorities such as church and state and has assumed more responsibility for his own self-definition. This shift in emphasis from external to internal authority is one of the major changes of our time.

Man's self-concept, his views of nature, and his ideas about art have been profoundly affected by this shift, and this has contributed to an identity crisis. We need only to look at the great social unrest or at the rapid changes in the meaning of art. These crises are the result of accelerating gaps between hopes and realities, ideals and actualities, between progress in knowledge of man and his increasing capability for self-destruction. "For in all parts of the world, the struggle now is for the *anticipatory development of more inclusive identities.* . . ." (Erik Erikson)

In what follows, learning in art is equated with growth in self-identity; that is, the work of art defines the student as he defines it, and some of the obvious dynamics of finding one's identity in art are analyzed. Also discussed are the reasons that the establishment of fundamentals or absolutes in art and art education are self-limiting. In addition, our need as teachers to understand the dy-

namics of change and our responsibility to encourage
change in our students, as well as within ourselves, are
examined.

In art and art teaching, there is an increasing gap
between the aesthetics of the past and the present. Traditional art ideas have become less and less useful in
defining the art forms needed to express the psychic
tensions of today. We acknowledge, for example, the
unsuitability of the representational forms of the sixteenth century. Yet, some instructors teach life drawing
as if the conceptions of form and figure have not sub-
stantially changed since the Renaissance. Even present-
day aesthetics are changing rapidly. To some artists,
Abstract Expressionism no longer suitably expresses the
paradoxes, ironies, and anxieties of contemporary life,
while to others it expresses them much too well. The
open-ended compositional situation of an Expressionistic
abstraction only adds further to an artist's sense of ambi-
guity and frustration. Then, hard-edge geometric paintings and the unambiguous satire of Pop art might best
establish a sense of security where none seems to exist.
Pop art editorializes against the superficial and fixed
interpretations of creativity in art, especially when it is
understood on a comic book level; the codification of
aesthetic responses, which the cataloguers of the past
would impose on the present, does not offer sacrosanct
criteria for the cultivation of experience today. Minimal
art is equally insistent that clarity of thinking today is
absolutely essential and proceeds to deal with the po-
lemics of phenomenological visual responses. In the art
classrooms students are impatient with formulas, traditional "fundamentals," and ready-made answers, no
matter how they are sugarcoated with phrases about
self-expression and creativity. Students are tired of lip-
service generalities, realizing that art taught in the classroom is often at odds with the stated ideals and goals

of art education. They are discovering that many of the newer concepts of art, often ignored in the classroom, offer important opportunities for clarifying their ideas about the way they feel about themselves and about contemporary life. Under inner stress they seek personal help in dealing with ways of expressing and organizing emotions in art in order to make more sense out of them. Many of the older teaching techniques are inadequate and they quickly recognize this. They are having trouble reconciling their feelings, attitudes, and activities in the classroom with those outside of the classroom. Difficulties with conflicting and repressed drives erupt in identity confusions, and profoundly affect what and how we teach. Let us see why.

Under emotional stress a person may become alienated from his real self. He may then reallocate his major energies in organizing himself according to á rigid system of inner emotional dictates. He confines himself to a "straitjacket." He ignores his particular potential, the depth and clarity of his own thoughts and feelings, interests and wishes; the ability to express himself fully; the possibility of exploiting his willpower and inner resources; and his ability to realize his special gifts and capabilities. Instead of a spontaneous and growing integration of his personality, he forces on himself an inhibitory, destructive, and artificial integration. In art, this manifests itself in innumerable ways. For instance, there is the child who, after painting a spontaneous landscape in color, insisted on covering it with black and said: "I want to blot out my picture because I don't feel I can do anything myself that is worthwhile." Or look at the artist who survived a German concentration camp who said: "I paint Op pictures because they require fewer decisions and, consequently, fewer moments of anxiety." (There are many reasons that an artist will use one type of visual form rather than another and neither Op art nor hard-edge painting, or any other art form can automatically be associated with one kind of personality or another. Human responses are too complex and too personal for such broad generalities even though individual instances seem to support them.)

We become ourselves—that is, we define ourselves—through particular action; we choose ourselves in each act of growth and development. Consciousness of our identity as a self is not simply an intellectual idea. We cannot simply accept an idea, such as that of Descartes, "I think, therefore, I am." We are not simply an idea, but a complex variety of self-awarenesses that are revealed in the roles we play and the conceptualizations we make; in the self-images we hold; and in the symbolic projections we employ in our works of art. The artist defines himself and his aesthetic perceptions by each decision he makes in his work. Each color, line, shape, and the relationships created with them, each perceptual integration made at every moment in the development of his work becomes a part of his expressive self and his expression in art. Self-awarenesses of sensations and sensitivities, as they relate to each other through the work of art, increase and define aesthetic and creative identity.

We must clarify our teaching methods. The teacher can be easily confused about the relationship between creativity and learning. He may still dictate how and what an art student should learn, either directly by the kinds of assignments he makes, or indirectly by his aesthetic projections while criticizing a student's work. He may feel that progress in learning and creativity will not take place unless clearly defined within the limits of specific ideas, insights, problems, and definitions that he proposes to the class. Yet, important creativity comes from the student's own self-motivated inspirations, dreams, hopes, goals, fantasies, frustrations, conflicts, and daydreams.

How can the complexities of the individual student be handled in terms of a learning situation in the art classroom? The key is the *self*. Students want to face you, and you them, not with the mask of professionalism, but as a person with whom they can relate in both joy and despair. Can the instructor tap the student's own inner forces that motivate him and focus the student's attention, sense of importance, and his problem-solving abilities on these inner dynamics? Can he help the student to see how these relate in disciplined ways to problems of visual control? If he can, the shift of control in the classroom is from his dictates to those of the student. The student becomes more and more responsible for understanding the complexities of art. How many courses are now taught, even in the lower elementary grades, as if certain "basic fundamentals," such as principles of design, color-harmony theories, medium techniques, and realistic drawing skills, are the primary bases and sources for self-expression and the creative organization of feelings and thoughts in art. How many students begin turning out acceptable designs, acceptable compositions, acceptable drawings that primarily mirror the taste, aesthetics, and standards of the instructor? Contrived, tight, slick works of art often result from this kind of teaching.

There is often in the minds of instructors a mystique about teaching based on the idea that only a logical sequence of ideas, analyses, visual aids, techniques—defensible to a curriculum committee—will produce learning. But the logic of the instructor is not necessarily the same as that of the student. The empirical, subjective, experimental, and emotional explorations of the student, based on his personal observation and discoveries, must be respected. The instructor's association of ideas, sequences of thought, and readiness for analyses, critiques, and awarenesses have a "life of their own" and are not necessarily those of the student. Although they can influence the student, they should not be dictated, otherwise, educational crises in a democratic society can easily occur.

Identity confusion develops when there is a disunity of the self. When one's ideal self-image meshes with his view of his actual self, there is unity. When they do not mesh, there is disunity and confusion. How does self-identity function in the classroom? When the self-concepts of the student as an individual, as a human being as a student, and as a potential artist are respected by the teacher, when self-integration and self-respect are encouraged, then self-identity is clarified and strengthened. The student knows whether or not he is learning and he respects the teacher who in turn respects him. Authentic self-identity is encouraged when the focus is on the individual student and the interactive processes between him and the teacher, without imposition of direct or implied standards.

Even John Dewey, as emphatic as he was about individual creativity, tied his educational philosophy to a priori concepts of behavior: "If we are willing to conceive education as the process of forming fundamental dispositions, intellectual and emotional, toward nature and fellowmen, philosophy may even be defined as the general theory of education." (Ralph Harper, "Significance of Existence and Recognition for Education," chapter VII in N. B. Henry, ed., *Modern Philosophies and Education,* 54th Yearbook of the National Society for the Study of Education [Chicago: Published by the Society, 1955], p. 245.) In other words Dewey believed in "forming fundamental dispositions." Rather than true freedom of choice, the student must learn what is taught to him based on the fundamental dispositions decided for him by the instructor. This philosophy lays the foundation for all kinds of imposed learnings despite protestation to the contrary and the most careful attempts to define creative objectives. Who exactly is to decide what the fundamental dispositions toward a work of art should be? Despite the fundamental dispositions of the critics and the majority of his countrymen, van Gogh forged ahead to create new dispositions.

The student in the art classroom must be encouraged to work with those feelings, ideas, and sensations that to him are most meaningful. He must feel free to work along those lines that make the most sense. The role of the teacher then becomes one of helping him to form his own ideas and experiences; develop his own experiments, problems, and theories; try his own techniques, procedures, and self-disciplines.

Learning takes place in relationship to new ideas, new behavioral patterns, and new situational stimuli, whether introduced by the teacher or by the student himself. The instructor has a very strong and firm function. Teaching is not laissez-faire. When he introduces a new idea it is his responsibility to present it with all the clarity he can and relate it as intimately and poignantly as possible to the ideas of the student. When he responds to a student's work he must bring in those ideas that seem to be most relevant to the student's understanding, direction, and experience. But his goal is guidance rather than stimulus-response, conditioned-reflex behavior. His emphasis is constantly on evoking the student into dialogues with himself. By guiding the student's thinking, he helps him see the possibility of new ideas and new behavioral responses. The instructor will change his teaching tactics, presentation of ideas, the degree of class permissiveness, even his approach to the individual student, in order to help him challenge himself. The teacher presents his

ideas firmly, but he is flexible in finding ways of clarifying them. If the student does not respond to the particular idea that he presents, he must be imaginative enough
to explore others with the student until he finds clues
and keys to the student's understanding. This is done
individually as well as collectively, through class discussions and class critiques. Students will find their own
level of learning, areas of success, and self-integration
when the teaching situation emphasizes their individuality.

The major characteristics of the processes involved in
self-identity are choice, anxiety, responsibility, and freedom. Free choice is essential. The moment one interferes
with this, authority is taken away from the individual.
Self-responsibility is anxiety ridden, because the student
makes his own choices. He can no longer look to or depend on external authority. He must look to his own
decisions and face their consequences. The student is
asked to face himself directly, authentically. No mickey-
mousing, no apple-polishing, and no completing assignments merely for the sake of doing them and no failures
in seeing relevancies. Emphasis is on arguments with
oneself rather than with unsympathetic adversaries.

Where art ends and self begins is not easy to discern,
but the dividing line is less important than the interactive dynamics between them and the processes that
help each define the other. To the degree that man is in
an identity crisis, his art is also. One of the main efforts
of contemporary art is that of attempting to define itself.
It sees itself externalized, as in the medium is the message, or as internalized, as in Conceptual art. In between
there is a whole score of polemic variations.

In the twentieth century, we have seen the emphasis in
art teaching shift from academic realism to creative self-
expression. We have not, however, seen sufficient clarification of how a student discovers his own path in art.

Self-expression is too vague a term. What self does one express? What expressive techniques should be used—cathartic, controlled, intellectual? And precisely what do these terms mean? As for the medium, exactly how should this be defined? The meaning of technique is also ambiguous. Should it refer exclusively to medium manipulation or should it include the organization of self-responses that help give life to the medium techniques? Should it be defined as a skill, or the very means by which expression takes place? Granted, answers to such questions are usually to be found in the relationships of these elements rather than either/or answers, but acknowledging such relationships does not necessarily clarify them. It is most important to examine the terms in which we state our ideas about art and teaching. Semantics can be confusing. Art teaching, to be effective, must deal with the whole person. The student must be helped to define his own identity. Art can then be an effective instrument of knowledge, a way of creating and communicating sensitive experiences and insights, and a means for authentic self-expression.

ART AND THE DISADVANTAGED *

Vincent Lanier

. . . .

Elsewhere in this volume, Carol Duncan examines some attitudes (and repercussions) faced in the academic environment when the goal is to educate the rich. In this article, Vincent Lanier takes a very critical look at prevailing attitudes toward so-called disadvantaged people and questions the type of art education they are getting.

Lanier criticizes the very term "culturally disadvantaged" and claims that ". . . poor people respond to and produce their own culture . . . [that] frequently embodies the same power and richness of image or phrase as middle-class art." Thus, taken along with Allen Leepa's comments (printed elsewhere in this book) that "important creativity comes from the student's own self-motivated inspirations, goals, and frustrations . . . ," we are led to believe that a deeper awareness of, as well as sympathy for, individual cultural conditions are essential in any valid and useful educational encounter.

Most researchers and theorists in art educa-

* Reprinted from *Art Education* (December, 1970).

Vincent Lanier, Professor and Head, Department of Art Education, University of Oregon, Eugene, Oregon. The photograph of the writer is superimposed over a digital plot of the Mona Lisa used as a visual theme in the Final Report of the Uses of Newer Media Project, of which he was Project Director.

tion fail to take the uniqueness and significance of individual cultural makeups into consideration in real and effective ways, as Lanier
demonstrates.

In this article Lanier cites several reports
concerning art education for the poor. He questions both the goals and the results of several
experiments. Finally, Lanier comes to a radical
conclusion—one that will not sit well with traditional artists or educators who see art as the
most significant activity of a society. In answer
to the question of just what art should do for
slum and ghetto children, he notes: "What the
teaching of art must do and can do is to help
the poor . . . confront and explore their own
problems. This cannot be done by conceiving
of art as the central behavior of society or of
the individual."

Lanier, along with most of the other contributors to this volume, is dissatisfied with
art education today, which he feels "has been
notably unimaginative in generating concepts
of curricula to confront today's problems . . ."
"The dispossessed of our society want dignity
even more than good jobs and suburban
homes."

Vincent Lanier has taught at several colleges, and contributed articles to the Journal
of the National Art Education Association,
as well as numerous art education journals.
He is head of the Department of Art Education of the University of Oregon, Eugene, Oregon.

. . . .

Except for those who are literally handicapped, there are no disadvantaged people. There are only those who are differentially advantaged. In a society with the present level of interpenetration of class values, the concept of what is a cultural advantage cannot be rigid. The classical sociological idea of upward social mobility toward a fixed desirable norm must be replaced by a nonhierarchical continuum of competing life-styles. The flavor of soul food can please even the middle-class palate.

The first principle of education for the children of the rural and urban poor is to look at them as possessors of different advantages rather than as cultural paupers. The dominant principle of art education for these children is to recognize the merits of the aesthetic experiences they already have had and are having. To approach differentially cultured children in any other way, or at least from the direction we now approach them, is to demean and offend them and, indeed, to fail in our efforts as educators.

It is our intention in this paper to argue the necessity of looking at the "problem" of the education of the poor from a point of view different from what is commonly held, to examine some of the ways in which art has been used—improperly or ineffectually—to help the children of the poor, and to suggest one role the visual arts might play in providing the poor, and perhaps all of us, with what we need and want from society.

THERE ARE NO CULTURALLY DISADVANTAGED

To say that there are no culturally disadvantaged is not to say that there are no poor in America, or that poverty has no negative aspects. To live in substandard housing, attend inferior schools, eat inadequate food, lack appropriate medical care—these kinds of deprivations, particularly in the midst of plenty, are unfortunate and unnecessary. These experiences, however, do not inevitably produce ignorance, the inability to think critically, or an absence of responsiveness to one's verbal, visual, and musical surroundings. On the contrary, poor people respond to and produce their own culture, which, while it may be "simple" and unsophisticated, frequently embodies the same power and richness of image or phrase as middle-class art.

It is neither romanticizing nor patronizing to recognize the merits of slum conditioning, as well as to condemn its disadvantages. John Hurst, responding by letter to an article on the chemistry of learning (*Saturday Review*, January 20, 1968), writes:

> We can in no way conclude from this or other data that these children's brains were initially chemically or morphologically inferior to those of children from the standard culture, but simply that they were different in some dimensions. I suspect the stimulation and richness of the urban Negro child's environment is every bit as great as, and probably greater than, that of the white child in a suburban housing tract.
>
> The danger in emphasizing the development of stimulating and enriched environments is that they will become standard and fixed in terms of the values of the dominant culture. Thus we will emerge with another powerful tool to reduce individual differences and to enhance a standard conformity in our society. We are just beginning to think of developing schools and programs that reflect the culture of the child rather than futilely trying to develop the child to fit the school; it would be a tragedy to have this healthy bit of progress reversed under the guise of optimizing the biochemical development of the brain.[1]

[1] John G. Hurst (responding by a Letter to the Editor to an article on the chemistry of learning) *Saturday Review*, March 16, 1968, p. 62.

Speaking of the Rios family, Oscar Lewis writes of his attitude toward the Puerto Rican poor both on their native island and in New York City:

> In spite of the presence of considerable pathology, I am impressed by the strengths of this family. I am impressed by their fortitude, vitality, resilience and ability to cope with problems which would paralyze many middle-class individuals. It takes a great deal of staying power to live in their harsh and brutalizing environment. They are a tough people, but they have their own sense of dignity and morality and they are capable of kindness, generosity and compassion.[2]

From a different point of view a sociologist describes his three years of living experiences in the inner-city and suggests that the density and diversity of the slum promotes a highly refined and well-ordered social structure. The slum is unlike the suburbs in its values, but it is no less coherently articulated. Nor are the children of the slums ignorant; they have different knowledges and skills than the children of the suburbs.[3]

One area of both knowledge and skill in which ghetto children are differentially advantaged rather than disadvantaged is language. A linguist makes the following comment:

> The syntax of low-income Negro children differs from standard English in many ways, but it has its own internal consistency. Unfortunately, the psychologist, not knowing the rules of Negro nonstandard English, has interpreted these differences not as the result of well-learned rules but as evidence of "linguistic underdevelopment." He has been handicapped by his assumption that to develop language is synonymous with the development of the psychologist's own

[2] Oscar Lewis, *La Vida* (New York: Random House, 1955), pp. xxix, xxx.

[3] Gerald D. Suttles, *The Social Order of the Slum* (Chicago: University of Chicago Press, 1968).

form of standard English. Thus he has concluded that if Black children do not speak like white children they are deficient. One of the most blatant errors has been a confusion between hypotheses concerning language and hypotheses concerning cognition. For this reason, superficial differences in language structures and language styles have been taken as manifestations of underlying differences in learning ability. To give one example, a child in class was asked, in a test of simple contracts, "Why do you say they are different?" He could not answer. Then it was discovered that the use of "do you say," though grammatically correct, was inappropriate to his culture. When he was asked instead, "Why are they different?" he answered without hesitation at all.[4]

It is interesting to wonder if theorists and researchers in art education have not made a similar error, namely that of confusing hypotheses concerning culture-bound visual literacy with hypotheses concerning cognition. In light of comments like these, any ordered and reasonable thinking or planning about the education of the children of the poor must consider recognition of their capabilities and their values, both moral and aesthetic. This does not mean that the middle-class teacher must adopt these values or systems for himself or act as if he has done so. Indeed, one cannot "kid" these children, part of whose survival mechanisms include a high level of perception of our American caste arrangements.

PRESENT ROLE OF ART FOR THE DISADVANTAGED

That there are a multitude of ideas and programs designed to "help" disadvantaged youngsters through art needs no demonstration. What is shocking is not the lack of goodwill, energetic programs, or even money, but,

[4] Joan C. Baratz, "The Language of the Ghetto Child," *The Center Magazine*, Vol. II, No. 1 (January, 1969), p. 32.

rather, the amazing lack of insight or imagination. Almost invariably, art is seen as some sort of magical balm; once the children of the poor are dipped in it, they will be more like our children and, thus, acceptable to our society.

The error of this thinking starts far back in our conception of the arts (the middle-class arts, of course) as the central function of human behavior. As naïve as this idea may sound when stated baldly, it recurs repeatedly in the literature on art and art education. For example:

> The practical educator has been skeptical—and he still is —about the place art can have in an American educational program, but actually, art not only has a role in education; *art is education*. This basic fact has not been stressed frequently or vigorously enough . . . Who would be so foolish as to attempt to minimize the place of Socrates, Plato and Aristotle; of Herodotus? No true educator would try to detract from these men who have, indeed, lighted up the ages. But a sophisticated teacher knows also that the works of the masters of the age of Pericles were hewn in eternal stone, etched in clay, and crystallized in dance and drama—they received the breath of life from the artist. He is fully aware that education is in the arts; that they are the source, that the desirable whole is the totality of all learning.[5]

This kind of arrogant assumption of the central function of the arts ignores a host of other behaviors and contexts through which men negotiate their environments, many of which can be far more important for these tasks than the arts. One obvious example is language, both spoken and written; another, of course, is science.

However, in the context of the subject of this paper, a somewhat similar thought, though hedged with reservations, appears in the final report of the conference on Art

[5] Albert Christ-Janer and Ralph L. Wickiser, "Higher Education and the Arts," *The Arts in Higher Education*, Dennis and Jacob, eds. (San Francisco, Calif.: Jossey-Bass Inc., 1968), pp. 44, 45.

and the Disadvantaged sponsored by the Office of Education and held at Gaithersburg, Maryland, in 1966:

> Some specialists in mathematics, physical education, or foreign languages might insist at a conference that their field was of the first importance, that it was basic and indispensable to the child's education; but they would not come up with the range of uses and values claimed by the artists and art educators at this art conference. This distinction emerged as one of the principal themes of the conference: that the arts, unlike other school subjects, can engage the whole person in an experience of unusual depth and delight, with effects that are complex, multiple, and powerful. Stated another way, the contribution of the arts to education is vaguer and harder to define than the contribution of the better established subjects. This vagueness, however, derives not from the ineffectiveness of the arts but from their very richness.[6]

Later in the document, one of the participants makes this statement:

> . . . I think it can be shown that the most consummately adequate model of proper education in all subjects is the model of the well-run art classroom: where each one's talents are relevant; where every child's products are valued equally insofar as they emanate from equally worthy children; where children are not pitched competitively against each other, nor denigrated or honored for "higher achievements"; where each proceeds in accordance with his own unique tempo of development; and where at any given moment the child moves on to tasks for which he is ready, as defined by his own prior work and achievements. If all classrooms were run with these as the main guidelines to the relationships of students, curriculum, and teachers, it seems indubitable that our schools would rise to heights of excellence they have no chance of achieving under the present average mode

[6] Judith Murphy and Ronald Gross, *The Arts and the Poor*, a report of the U.S. Office of Education sponsored conference on the Role of the Arts in Meeting the Social and Educational Needs of the Disadvantaged, 1968, p. 8.

of conduct. I am saying, in effect, that the model of the art experience is the model of true educational experience in all subjects.[7]

It is interesting to note that Tumin's eloquent assessment of the art class neglects to examine the curriculum, "what" these children are engaged in producing or responding to. For if what he writes were indeed an accurate picture of the art class today, surely there would be a rush of pupils to enroll in such classes. There are "well-run art classrooms," with the characteristics Tumin specifies, and yet there is no evidence or indication that these classes attract or "hold" pupils better than others, the reason very likely being that the content of these classes is no more relevant and no more stimulating to youngsters today (particularly the children of the poor) than the content in other classrooms. To assume this lofty superiority for the subject of art—as it is used in the schools today—or the process of the teaching of art, is to promote false values and to denigrate (however inadvertently) the contributions of other sorts of human activities.

Another almost bizarre suggestion for using art to help the poor is the "Pied Piper" program. With some variations, this breed of program involves bringing the children of the poor into contact with a so-called creative artist. The artist "does his thing," the young watch or join in, and we have instant rehabilitation! It doesn't seem to matter much what this "thing" is. The important factor is the magic of the artist's presence, which in some unspecified way is supposed to promote mental health, good human relationships, and social and intellectual skills, and to eliminate the alleged bad effects of growing up poor in a rich society.

This position was articulated some years ago by Allan

[7] *Ibid.*, p. 10.

Kaprow (though in general terms, not restricted to the disadvantaged) and is clearly visible in the following paragraph.

What school children need is a Pied Piper, lots of Pied Pipers, not social workers and lab technicians. The Pied Piper had magic and this is what is important about his story. Like magicians, artists deal in a sort of magic, and it is proposed here that some of them can double as Pied Pipers and lead school children along roads they are pressured to avoid and soon forget. The objective is, therefore, to bring to the lower schools as many artists as possible, with no preconceived plan on our part of how they will conduct their classes. They themselves may have plans, but each artist will be responsible for his or her own approach . . . what we are proposing is an approach to art education which has in mind only an awareness of the basic mystery of art and a belief (supported by ample evidence) that artistic people are best suited for revealing this to youngsters.[8]

Later in the document, Kaprow expands his position during a question and answer period:

Mr. Kaprow: All because I have a couple of backyard magicians that I know. I propose that we turn them loose. Let's not worry about defining your criteria and your standards. That's the trouble with the whole blasted business up till now. You are making doilies and this and that, and it comes out awful.

Audience: No one here is interested in turning out doilies.

Mr. Kaprow: We reach a point where all verbage [*sic*] is verbage. Let's have a good show. Let's forget the definitions; afterward if you want to play around and see what happens, that's okay with me. I'm saying forget the verbage. I don't know how many times I can say it without your really thinking I'm lying, but I really mean that.

Audience: I get the feeling that you consider yourself the kind of Pied Piper that you are talking about—

[8] Edward Mattil, *A Seminar in Art Education for Research and Curriculum Development,* Final Report of U.S. Office of Education sponsored Cooperative Research Project V-002, 1966, pp. 84, 85.

Audience: I was just going to ask you if you could "role play" for us how you would go about your magic.

Mr. Kaprow: It takes me a little time to prepare my act.[9]

The same concept is repeated by one of the speakers a year later at the Gaithersburg conference noted before:

According to Mr. Roman, "the artist-teacher, because of his magical and myth-making qualities, as well as his craft discipline and dedication, . . . is almost inevitably a charismatic figure to adolescents." Further, he said, the artist, "because of his style and charisma, can often reach segments of the population inaccessible to traditional social service professionals," and "just as the clinician inevitably directs himself to pathology, the artist directs himself to health."

Several people took exception to the notion they felt implicit in the Roman paper: that the right things will begin to happen once you get a "person called an artist" involved. Mr. Roman persisted: "I would say as a generalization that, if we get professional artists involved in [ghetto] communities, things will start cooking." Later, after 'considerable spirited argument from educators working in the public schools, he modified his stand only slightly: "I think the answer is not every artist—we have to find the right artist; but I think the artist is the guy who can do it."[10]

The problems with this position are obvious, and not the least of them is that it represents a very high degree of anti-intellectualism. One doesn't think, one just does —and in this case one does art by following the leader. Somehow, since the artist is a magician, all will come right in the end. It would be difficult to take this position seriously, were it not for the large numbers of people, particularly in the visual arts, who appear to believe in it, at least if one can measure their beliefs by what they preach.

A third type of disadvantaged program distinguished by its frequency and high level of monetary support,

[9] *Ibid.*, pp. 86, 87.
[10] Judith Murphy and Ronald Gross, *op. cit.*, pp. 7, 8.

both federal and foundation, is what is sometimes called "cultural imperialism." As the Gaithersburg conference report puts it, " 'We've had it with bringing the Pittsburgh Symphony into the ghetto' proclaimed a veteran poverty worker. . . ." [11] As encouraging as this statement may appear, our hopes are shattered just ten pages later in the report as the next quotation will reveal.

> Could composition in visual arts also be taught this way, so that the student might learn to discriminate between good and bad composition, and eventually between paintings by expert and nonexpert artists? Could the student learn to appreciate the excellence of Shakespeare's poetry and dramaturgy by viewing two different presentations on videotape—one of a scene from Shakespeare and the other from a lesser dramatist? Or could he learn, through videotaped performances, to appreciate the characteristics of acting and production excellence by watching different theatre groups—an amateur community theatre, say, and a top professional company—perform the same dramatic scene? [12]

Why is it essential as a criterion of growth in aesthetic response to "appreciate the excellence of Shakespeare's poetry and dramaturgy," or classical music, romantic poetry, or Renaissance or hard-edge painting? Are there no arts in which the poor and their children now participate and toward which they manifest critical and discriminatory responses? Small wonder we "turn off" the children of the poor in our classrooms. Were our meaningful aesthetic experiences—yours and mine—to be regarded as trivial, as are theirs, we would be as disdainful and resentful. Until we learn that Lou Rawls and James Brown have as vital an artistic impact on the children of the poor as Beethoven and Brahms may have on the teachers of those children, we will fail in our classrooms and projects. Further, if the reader is a parent (and, par-

[11] *Ibid.,* p. 15.
[12] *Ibid.,* p. 25.

ticularly, a middle-class parent), let me ask him what his children are listening to today: Bach or Brown, the Beatles or Rossini? For the youth of all classes, rich as well as poor, artistic values are not quite so fixed as we middle-class adults believe them to be.

A fourth type of program in this context is the empirical research that attempts to investigate "disadvantaged" children's artistic behavior. Depending on the rigors with which the study is organized and proceeds, some very reliable data on some highly limited aspects of human behavior in art might be obtained. The trouble lies in the absence of priorities in our conception of research. Some research is more important to do now than other research. For example, empirical investigation of alternatives in art curriculum (indeed in all curriculum) are highly significant to meet today's problems in the schools. Studies on the psychology of perception, in artistic behavior, or in modes of curriculum organization or teaching methodology are not as significant today.

This is not to say the latter are intrinsically less worthwhile than the former, or that "practical" or applied research is more worthy than "pure" research. Some types of studies are simply more appropriate than others as bases to deal with the problems of the moment. For the most part, appropriate studies are not being carried out, at least not by people whose primary interest and obligation is the study of the teaching of art. Ideally, of course, both types of research should be done at the same time.

To illustrate research that may well be intrinsically worthwhile but is quite inappropriate to deal with the urgent problems of today's art classroom, let me quote this review:

> In an effort to understand the effect of child-rearing practices on children's attitudes and behavior in art, Alper,

Blaine, and Adams studied the finger-painting behavior of underprivileged and middle-class children. They speculated that the different ways that mothers of different social classes tried to train their children—especially toilet training—would affect the child's willingness to use fingerpaint, the amount of time he is willing to use it, whether he uses his finger or his whole hand, and whether he uses browns or blacks as well as other colors when given a choice.

The study revealed that underprivileged children are more willing to use fingerpaints than middle-class children, that they use the whole hand and smear more frequently, and that they use warm colors more often. Alper, Blaine, and Adams conclude from their study, which is far more detailed than this summary suggests, that early child-rearing practices do indeed influence the child's willingness to use certain art media and the way he uses them.[13]

The critical questions of whether or not these "certain art media" are appropriate to the children in question, or, more importantly, what is being explored and expressed by these media, is again ignored.

One might go on with this consistently distressing catalogue of ideas and programs for helping the children of the poor through art for some time. Perhaps it will suffice to mention only one specific addition here. This is the CASE (Contingencies Applicable for Special Education) project of Harold Cohen, which has been repeatedly publicized among art educators. This program is designed to rehabilitate delinquent boys and restore them to the "mainstream of the nation." As one report of the project explains it:

> As Mr. Cohen sees his job, it is not to change "the system" but to show his students how to select alternatives within the environment so as to beat it.
> By way of motivation, Mr. Cohen freely used the extrinsic rewards that society honors and his boys understand—mostly money. The program operated largely through rewards (con-

[13] *Ibid.*, pp. 20, 21.

tingencies) of this kind for achievement or improvement.
The boys got points, convertible into cash, which permitted
them to buy additional privileges, have visitors, use the
recreation lounge, and send money home. The academic
curriculum was mostly programmed, straight through from
first to twelfth grade. Students who didn't achieve anything
were not compelled to attend class, but they simply didn't
earn any points—and after seeing what the points would
buy and what they were missing, few kids remained "on relief" for long.[14]

Cohen claims further that, ". . . the visual-explora-
tion problems presented these students with a nonverbal
tool for examining the social and environmental conditions that surrounded these culturally deprived youngsters." One problem represented as a nonverbal tool is
described as follows:

In order to introduce the student to the problems that a
blank picture plane presents, I mimeographed four black
lines on hundreds of sheets of white paper, and I passed
them out. Each student had ten to twenty pieces of paper
with the same four lines on them. Everyone agreed that by
measurement the four lines were equidistant from each
other, meaning that they were parallel. I selected a few
examples out of a book on visual perception, and demonstrated how it was possible to make these four lines appear
nonparallel, to fool the eye. I took one of the sheets of
paper, taped it to the blackboard, and within a few minutes,
by adding new lines, I destroyed the illlusion of parallelism.
We spent quite some time talking about the phenomenon
and what was taking place. Here was a case where we knew
that the lines were parallel (we had measured them), but
that by adding new lines, by visual manipulation, we made
the truth appear false. They were rather excited by this
system of "faking it," and I asked them to try other means
of destroying the parallelism of these four lines. I gave them
a ball-point pen as the tool because it had none of the arty
connotations of a brush, and it was safe.
At the end of the first session I taped each student's work

[14] *Ibid.*, pp. 30, 31.

on the wall, and we talked about whether each one worked
or not. Did the lines still appear parallel? Some did; some
didn't. This led into a discussion of what it takes to change
not only four lines but anything that exists in space by adding or removing something to or from it. I made lots of "for
instances," using all kinds of subject matter, but ending
with people.[15]

This misrepresentation of an exercise in perception as
a nonverbal tool for examining social and environmental
conditions would be tolerable if it were not a very common error among those in the visual arts. The activities
Cohen reports—such as the one quoted—are nonverbal
tools for examining the mechanics of visual organization,
and no more than that save by analogy, as his last sen-
tence and particularly the last phrase ("but ending with
people") clearly indicates.

Much worse than this frequent and unfortunate error,
however, is Cohen's rationale for the entire project as
explained in the first quotation. For an educator (he calls
himself an educational ecologist) to accept "the system"
without question, show young people how to "beat it,"
and reinforce this behavior with rewards of money, is to
pander to the most unsavory aspects of the American
mainstream value structure. It would be bad enough to
contaminate wholesome ends with these ignoble means,
but one must even question the merit of the ends he
seeks.

Perhaps a significant postscript to present activity in
the area of our concern can be noted in Silverman's report of a large-scale empirical investigation testing art
curricula designed for "disadvantaged youth." He writes,
"This study has demonstrated that the assumption that
art education practices are profitable experiences simply

[15] Harold L. Cohen, "Learning Stimulation," *Art Education,*
Journal of the National Art Education Association, Vol. 22, No. 3
(March, 1969), p. 7.

because of their concrete, nonverbal nature is erroneous." [16]

WHAT ART SHOULD DO FOR THE CHILDREN OF THE POOR

What the teaching of art must do and can do is to help the poor—particularly the children of the poor—confront and explore their own problems. This cannot be done by conceiving of art as the central behavior of society or of the individual. It is not. This cannot be done by seduction into a dream world via Pied Piperism. The hunger of belly or spirit is very real. This cannot be done by the painfully slow process of empirically cataloguing and connecting the behavior patterns of the act of art (its response or creation), as necessary as this procedure ultimately may be. This cannot be done by training the young to a more effective assessment of their' visual surroundings except as these surroundings involve the impact of other people. The dispossessed of our society want dignity even more than good jobs and suburban homes.

What then do we do for the disadvantaged? First of all, we stop thinking of them as disadvantaged and accept as valid art experiences the arts they already enjoy and approach critically. Secondly, we must understand by continual exposure, the life-styles, the languages, the cultural patterns of the poor so that they will neither surprise nor shock us when we meet these patterns as teachers in the classroom. Third, we must learn to construct means—in this case in the art class—by which the children of the poor can explore their own life problems and develop alternatives to alienation, frustration, and irrational violence.

[16] Ronald Silverman, *Developing and Evaluating Art Curricula Specifically Designed for Disadvantaged Youth,* Final Report of the U.S. Office of Education sponsored Project No. 6-1657, 1969, p. 68.

Without conceiving of the visual or any arts as some kind of magical panacea for all the myriad problems of human life, teachers of art and others in related fields must approach the children of the rural and urban poor from a new perspective, one that embodies the primary concepts of this paper. Further, new concepts of curriculum must structure the activities of the art classroom, particularly on the secondary level.

Although it must be noted that art education—the study of the teaching of art—has been notably unimaginative in generating concepts of curricula to confront to-day's problems, there are at least a few proposed new models or directions in the field. Among these one might include: (1) a cluster of curricular patterns broadening the study of art into the study of the humanities and called in some cases "aesthetic education"; (2) curricula shifting the balance of their content toward a more equitable distribution of time spent on studio, historical, and critical activities; (3) a focusing of emphasis within traditional curricula upon experiences designed to develop cognitive and, in particular, perceptual competencies; (4) the study and reorganization of the physical environment and those cues in the environment that may tend to affect covert and overt behavior; (5) the use of the popular arts—most particularly the film arts—as content in the art class and as vehicles for emotive explorations of new alternatives in human relationships.

Only the last two conceptions (4 and 5) represent radical or innovative directions. The first three, in the main, can be best seen as refinements of existing domains in the teaching of art, both as regards means and ends. Nor are they, except peripherally, equipped to confront the explosive social problems of the present. Of the last two ideas, the fifth and final one [17] appears to this author to

[17] See Vincent Lanier, "The Teaching of Art as Social Revolution," *Phi Delta Kappa*, Vol. L, No. 6 (February, 1969), pp. 314–319.

contain the possibilities for development without which the teaching of art can contribute little to the education of the children of the poor and in any substantial sense to the formal schooling of all but a very few of middle-class youngsters as well.

One possible development in this area might be called filmmaking as social theorizing. The function of film as social theory can be analogous to the development and testing of hypotheses in any theory building. Problem-solving usually begins with the observation of a problem and the accumulation of all available relevant data clarifying the problem. With cinema, the manifestations of the problem in visual and dramatic form would be filmed. If, for example, the problem were the resolution of group conflicts by gang "rumble," such a point of conflict would be staged with all of its ramifications and filmed.

The next step is to construct a hypothesis, a plausible guess as to how the problem might be solved. In any complex situation such as one involving social relationships, a number of hypotheses may need to be developed. In cinema, this would be a nonfilm step, except insofar as the filmmakers would refer to the presentation of the problem in film in order to construct their own or several hypotheses. Using the example of the gang fight again, the filmmakers would conceive of seemingly viable alternatives to combat resulting from group conflicts.

Once a guess or hypothesis has been developed, most thoughtful procedures require that the hypothesis be tested in some way in order to determine how effectively it serves to solve the problem. In physical sciences such as chemistry, for example, chemicals are combined and the resulting compound applied to the actual situation for which it was prepared. One classical illustration is Dr. Ehrlich's salvarsan or compound #606, which was literally the 606th compound tested in the treatment of syphilis. In the social sciences, where such precise testing is impossible and any testing extremely difficult at present, social theory might be tested in symbol form by acting out the test of the hypothesis in dramatic form. Thus, the filmmakers would construct, act out, and record on film another way of settling the conflict that led to the gang fight. This might be done by following a carefully planned script or by having the actors improvise within the limitations of the hypothetical solution. If more than one hypothesis is to be tested, several such dramatizations might be organized, acted out, and filmed.

Needless to say, such testing in symbol form does not replace empirical testing. Social theories—like any other theories—must be tested in life situations, even though such testing itself rarely provides a definitive assessment. In one sense the Eighteenth Amendment to the Constitution, or Prohibition, in its passage and subsequent repeal was an empirical test of the utility, and by implication the desirability, of federal regulation of the manufacture, sale, and transportation of alcoholic beverages. In the same sense any social project or program provides a test situation. Most commonly our only means of examining the possibilities of success or failure of a social project before it is initiated is by discussion; by the manipulation of verbal symbols. What is being suggested here is the addition of a specific tool, that of filmmaking, as a form of testing by the manipulation and recording of dramatic symbols.

Since this process clearly involves current technology, it might not be too fanciful to consider the use of television as a possible alternative or addition to the motion-picture camera. Videotape and the television camera provide unique benefits in the form of instant replay, re-use of the same tape after erasure, as well as permanent recording. Perhaps one adaptation of the process of using film as social theorizing would be to use television to test dramatizations of several possible hypotheses, reserving edited film for the permanent and aesthetically appropriate record of the most successful one.

In summary, this paper pleads for a reorientation of our attitudes toward the children of the poor, in the direction of recognition that they are differentially advantaged rather than disadvantaged. It calls for an acceptance of the arts that poor people enjoy—mainly the popular arts—as appropriate for the curriculum of the schools. It asks that we explore new possibilities in art curriculum such as the use of filmmaking as social theorizing. Finally, it attempts to expose the sometimes shabby, often inept, and always inadequate current practices in using art to help poor children.

ART EDUCATION: IN AND OUT OF SCHOOL *

Irving Kaufman

• • • • • • • • • • • • • • • • • • •

This article will prove of interest to all teachers, both in and out of art, as well as all students, in art as well as other subjects. It will interest both artists and art educators because of the broad range of questions, concerning traditional procedures, that are introduced by the author.

Kaufman observes that one of those factors necessarily limiting to the range and scope of art-educational activity is the architectural confines of the schoolroom itself. And he adds that the educational fiats that ". . . do not permit certain art activities because they are messy, disturbing, or suspiciously irreverent of school norms" harm art education's enormous potential.

He goes on to question an educational philosophy that "insists upon an extended art experience for all school children" and indicates that such a philosophy may be ". . . irrelevant and unnecessarily coercive." Furthermore he points out that many students

* Reprinted from *The Wisconsin Monographs of Visual Arts Education*, No. 2 (Spring, 1971).

Irving Kaufman

are involuntarily enrolled in art programs, with the result that ". . . there are negative considerations that flow from involuntary scheduling of art."

The desirability of teacher certification is questioned and the author indicates that such certification practices that are in effect today may tend to negate a desirable relationship between art education and art—a relationship that ". . . needs to be open, challenging, and pegged at a high level of excellence."

As far as curriculum is concerned, Kaufman observes: "Even in the best of school art situations, it is difficult to escape an air of lesson-plan contrivance, an undercurrent of anxiety about educational goals and a tendency toward curricular propriety."

Irving Kaufman, Professor of Art Education at the City College, City University of New York, has published articles in numerous journals, including Arts in Society *and* Art Education. *He is president of the Institute for the Study of Art in Education.*

. . . .

One of the most potent questions asked by the contemporary critics of education is, need education be equated with schooling? The presumption has been that any schools organized in a graded and curricular manner offer the appropriate means of educating individuals. Such a system of academic organization has accounted for the larger part of a student's intellectual development; it has exerted, as well, a commanding influence upon social and aesthetic growth. Yet it is commonplace today to note that schools have failed in both a philosophic as well as a pedagogic sense to "educate" large numbers of youngsters. There is as well a nagging doubt as to the efficacy of schooling even where it is nominally successful as in the "silent majority" of middle- and upper-class milieus. The most ardent apologist for the public as well as much of the private school systems would be hard pressed to point to many stable student bodies, secure in their own knowledge and equilibrium, fundamentally sure of the values of their culture. It also would be difficult to identify any large-scale movement toward mature social independence, cultivated sensibilities, or new cultural conditions sparked by the challenge and substance of schools. Though there are increasing numbers of students crammed full of facts, figures, and general edification, there are parallel feelings of bewilderment, uncertainty, anger, and a lack of esteem for the educational establishment. Schooling and education may indeed develop in differing directions, functioning frequently at cross-purposes with one another.

There is more than a suspicion that schools reinforce an academic and social distortion through their formal curricular patterns of organization; that there are arbitrary and coercive dimensions within the schoolish context that create obstacles to natural learning. A frequently accepted model of reductive and standardized teaching methodology furthers the programmatic pressures of the school. This provides an official academic repertory for teachers and students alike, which tends to be fragmented, predetermined, and even philistine, despite the extraordinary convolutions of American culture outside of the schoolhouse. Yet somehow, the natural resilience of youth makes itself felt. Education in its fullest sense does often occur, even if with a touch of frenzy and more than a touch of revolt. The youthful individual is alert to the "incidental" events and conditions of his or her surroundings of social turbulence, technological pervasiveness, and changing aesthetic dynamics. He becomes involved with feelings and sensibilities as a complement to an objectified cognition. Relevance is sought as students make excursions into experience outside of the normal and systematized school situations. The challenge of extra-school conditions and possibilities: subjective probings, drugs, militant political action, religious or spiritual phenomenon, participatory forms of art, as well as unconventional intellectual explorations all become grist for the contemporary student's education on all age levels. There is no telling what will be ground in such an unorthodox mill, but the issues have been joined. Sources outside of school have preempted many of the educative functions for good or for bad, with contradictory aspects of mindless conditioning as well as animated learning in varying dimensions. The pervasiveness of mass media and popular culture thus forces such questions as: Are schools as they are now constituted the most appropriate vehicles for education or have they become antiquated contradictory institutions unable to function honestly as social instruments of education? Is it necessary to modify the organizational patterns of schools or should there be supplementary means of education to fulfill needs to which the schools cannot properly respond?

It is against such a backdrop that art education responds to a number of alternative directions or philosophical guidelines by which it can pursue its goals. Art education has never been a central article of faith in the narrowly pragmatic schoolman's hierarchy of values. Nevertheless, with the increasing spread of the arts as an important element of a mass-based popular culture as well as in elite, sophisticated circles, there has been increased supportive and research attention given to the substance and means of art education. Much of this attention has focused upon the role of art education in

the schools. Despite this focus upon schools, which attention carries funds as well as "expertise," there has been a
substantial increase in art education in extra-school situations as well. This latter spread of educational opportunity is not a new one in art education. Museums and
their departments of education, community centers, social organizations such as the "Y," and various other
institutions external to the schools have had a long history of catering to the special artistic aspirations and
extracurricular needs of students. Recently, however,
the pace of extra-school art programs has quickened.
There has been a major expansion of opportunities for
students of all ages and levels in the traditional centers.
Further opportunities have appeared in such places as
storefront art studios and other novel and impromptu
"ateliers" of artistic activity, stimulated and supported
by new federal funds and the interest of the Office of
Education and the National Foundation on the Arts
and Humanities.

The quickening and expansion of art education outside of formal school environments may be seen as a
natural and complementary extension into the community of artistic activities that schools, for one reason or
another, cannot support. Such an attitude envisages good
will and mutual supportiveness from all sides, positing
a partnership in educational enterprise. Another attitude, however, suggests that the schools have largely
failed in providing opportunities for genuine individual
expressiveness, artistic creativeness, and critical aesthetic
responsiveness. Such a view seriously questions the ambiance of the school as one within which a student could
genuinely engage in expressive behavior. Thus it becomes necessary to establish openly generative and exploratory centers of art education outside of the supposed restrictive curricular and graded structuring of
schools. This, so as to encourage the natural propensities

of individual students toward personal expressiveness and the critical faculties necessary to visual literacy. Consequently, this latter view would look to the loosely structured extra-school art programs as replacing or counteracting the more systematized art education activities that prevail in regular schools.

It may be helpful to comment briefly upon some structural or otherwise operative considerations of both the school and extra-school art programs. To point up broadly the contrasting relationships or differing characteristic patterns of both types of programs may set the stage for a salutary interaction.

The school art programs have had a history for about a century now, starting officially with Massachusetts' importation from Britain of William Smith after the Civil War. There had been major philosophic movement within this period as to the role of art education. Initially, school art activities were regarded as leading to desirable skills that would extend industries: source of enlightened labor but also the students' vocational possibilities and manual dexterity. This changed generally at the turn of the century into an art for art's sake position that was to provide a beginning appreciation of culture for the masses. More recently, art education was looked upon as a means of personal and psychological expressiveness, an attitude in which Victor Lowenfeld played a major role in fostering creative expressiveness. There was more than a hint of therapy in some of the developmental theories of art education, though these were countered by a democratic belief in less clinical attitudes that called for the inherent self-actualization of the individual student. Most recently, there has been a coalescing of all of the previous positions into an integrated whole with an added conceptual emphasis upon the critical response to art, generally called aesthetic education.

The extra-school art programs have had almost as long a history, though not as extensive a base of operations. Their philosophic positions have rarely been dignified in theoretical papers or educational commentary. However, it can be safely said that the extra-school art programs had integrated the various philosophic positions mentioned above at a much earlier date than did the schools. Whether with a recreational goal in mind or a more serious pursuit of creative experiences, a distinctive factor of the extra-school art programs has been a self-sufficiency of purpose. That is, the experience or activity of art was generally respected for its own sake, rather than regarding art as an instrument used for larger social or personal ends. This may have been as much due to the casual nature of extra-school art programs and the lack of an educational research apparatus with which to formalize attitudes and procedures. On a more positive note, these extra-school art programs aimed toward a radical empiricism—a desirable confrontation and engagement between the individual and his experience focused upon the formative qualities of art. Whatever its reason, extra-school arts programs fostered the intrinsic satisfactions of the art experience. The programs were not subjected in any great measure to academic or externally influenced structuring, thus escaping a resulting philosophical codification. Even the creative art programs, which have been fostered in so-called disadvantaged or ghetto areas in the hope that somehow they would influence academic progress, have not become primarily instrumental. They manage to retain an openness and characteristic verve that celebrates the intrinsic satisfactions of the art experience.

The essential distinction, from a philosophic vantage point, however, is that a school art program is one foundation stone in the complex school edifice, whereas the extra-school art program enjoys a separateness and rela-

tive wholeness that does not necessitate complicated patterns of pedagogical interrelationship. The school art
program is frequently a procedural aspect within a the-
orized system of education, one factor in the student's
claim upon a diploma. It is subject to the influences
and pressures from a multitude of sources. Many of these
sources are either unknowing and innocent in matters
of and/or tolerate art education for inappropriate and
compromised reasons. This does not suggest any dis-
respect or out of hand rejection of the large group of
art educators on school and college levels who have
labored long, hard, and with sensitivity to strengthen
and intensify the place of art in the curriculum. Yet,
the overall and methodical structure of the school curriculum does impose limitations that can restrict the
natural, creatively spontaneous possibilities of the role
of art in education. The individual student and his
uniqueness often is lost as the press of numbers and
theoretical efficiency melts that individual into conglom-
erate abstractions. On the other hand, extra-school art
programs are comparatively free from the more standardized restrictions found in school organization. For
one, the extra-school art programs are rarely linked to
any other pedagogical and curricular demands in terms
of time, space, or similar disposition of priorities. They
exist independently in places that concentrate primarily
upon the immediate and intimate experiences of art as
a focus of attention. The programs are often expedient
but innovative, growing out of an insouciant approach
to educational experiences. Consequently, there is a comparative pertinence of individual creative purpose in
extra-school art programs. They more closely reflect a
philosophy established through the emerging internal
necessities or innately functioning conditions of art
rather than one of theoretically imposed and continued
convenience.

There are many school classrooms in which zestful, delightful, and creative art programs may be witnessed. Art education, particularly on the elementary level, has succeeded in stimulating artistically pleasurable and genuinely imaginative programs. However, this is not a consistent or widespread pattern. Even in the best of school art situations, it is difficult to escape an air of lesson-plan contrivance, an undercurrent of anxiety about educational goals and a tendency toward curricular propriety.

The extra-school art programs tend to escape such confining concerns. There may be slovenly structure and an impulsive negligence of the larger developmental considerations as characteristic elements in the extra-school art programs. Nevertheless, they generally are possessed of a vitality and an aptness that more than offsets any lack of standardized educational structure. Their very expediency and openness are an outgrowth of the adventurous explorations into formlessness and chaos with which art grapples and then orders. The philosophical vantage point out of which extra-school art programs are usually fashioned is a generous one, hospitable to a wide range of personal and creative possibilities. These conditions are inherently geared toward experiencing art for its own sake. If the initial generous impulse is permitted to develop within the formative contexts of an uncluttered artistic experience, then critical awareness and qualitative responsiveness may also occur—goals to be desired for any educational pattern of organization.

There are a number of specific distinctions between school art programs and extra-school art programs that feed into the general philosophical characteristics that have been noted. The physical environment tends to be different, the personnel involved are usually distinctive in each instance and the student body is enrolled for varying reasons.

The school art programs are, of course, almost always operated on the school premises. This may be modified on rare occasions when a class visits a museum or is taken to see some local event of artistic significance. For the most part, however, the art activities are carried on in regular classrooms or, in more fortunate circumstances, in specially designed art rooms. The latter are not always inviolate. In many schools with specifically constructed art areas one finds such space converted to "more important and regular" classroom teaching. In any case, whether the art area is an old boiler room, an ordinary classroom, or the most modern school-studio environment, it is subject to the ubiquitous administrative and custodial pressures. Rules and regulations as to health measures, cleanliness, neatness, and all of the other next to godliness virtues make themselves felt. Now one cannot quarrel with such beneficial values. They are a part of middle-class schooling and indeed possess intrinsic merit. Yet somehow, they also possess an indoctrinating officiousness that tends to intimidate and inhibit the more freewheeling propensities of expressive behavior. More important, in many specific instances, institutional fiats do not permit certain art activities because they are messy, disturbing, or suspiciously irreverent of school norms. Art, within the confines of school, has to be acceptable to the janitor in matters of custodial care and well behaved in an administrative sense. It cannot "arbitrarily" spill out of its scheduled location, even if the spontaneous verve of creativeness indicates the need of more walls as Gully Jimson coveted in Joyce Carey's "The Horse's Mouth." The physical and official environment in school thus may be a prohibiting factor even in the most affluently conceived suburban situations.

Extra-school art programs are, on the other hand, very often housed in spaces that are completely committed to the activities of art. Of course, a Saturday morning or after-school museum and community center program cannot escape all of the constraints that are found in schools. Comparative order and cleanliness are also desirable conditions outside of school buildings. Nevertheless, there seems to be a greater physical and attitudinal permissiveness for creative enterprise in community center basements or museum classrooms. The most adaptable space for encouraging art education may exist even outside of the hospitable museums and community centers—in stores, abandoned houses (made safe for occupants), lofts, and similar physical environments. Extra-school art programs which are fortunate enough to be housed in such marginal but adaptive surroundings can design and utilize their space much as artists transform similar space into studios. The advantages are obvious and the consequent freedom of action frequently supports a stimulating and exploratory program. There is a psychological as well as a physical latitude that provokes an absorbed involvement. Certainly, the ongoing, lively atmosphere as well as the enthusiastic work that can be seen in storefront art centers or impromptu workshops suggests that place exerts a large measure of influence upon the students' necessity for creative and unrestricted elbowroom. Schools in large urban areas may be well advised to press into service available nearby space, which need not conform to traditional school policy. Similarly, other types of school systems can borrow the expedient attitude of extra-school art programs, improvising suitable studio environments within which students can make and do "their things" without the constraints of more orthodox administrative policing. The most serious drawback of extra-school art programs and their allotted space is financial in nature. There is frequently not enough money for space, equipment, and material; certainly not on the level afforded to schools. Only generous funding policies can remedy such situations.

Who can and should teach art in the schools has always plagued both the theoreticians of art education as well as the school hiring officials. The latter are understandably puzzled by some of the contradictory stances of art educators. Generally, it is accepted that trained art educators are the most suitable personnel—educators who pursue a course of studies both in art and in education. However, art is a widely ranging miscellany of disciplines.

Art education consequently is still uncertain as to the necessity of training in breadth as against the appropriateness of depth. More crucial is the nagging question that remains unresolved: shall a teacher of art in the schools be an artist first or first an educator? Can he be the latter without also being the former? To confuse the issue further, there is a school of thought which believes that, on the elementary level, it is the classroom teacher who is most competent to teach art, just as he or she is the universal solvent in reading, writing, and arithmetic. It may be this latter group on an administrative level is as much motivated by a tightfisted educational economics that will not support extra art specialists, yet is insistent upon the essential inclusion of art in the regular curriculum.

In any case, the teaching of art in the schools is almost always carried on by certified personnel. These are individuals who have met local or state requirements of educational background, whether as art specialists or as classroom generalists. In some states the certification is quite specific as to level, elementary, junior-high, or secondary. Generally, the art specialist is certified to teach from kindergarten through twelfth grade, and the elementary generalist can boast of from zero to four or six credit hours in art education methodology courses. Perhaps, more significant than the systems of certification is the aspirational quality of the students who choose art teaching in the schools as a career. Though they are not all unfrocked artists or second-best art students, there is a tendency in art education to discourage the more active and serious student artists in colleges and those with unconventional enthusiasms. This is needlessly underscored where art education is structured independent of art departments at the college level. In a similar vein, serious art students rebel against what they consider to be excessive education requirements. They feel the need of more legitimate studio and history courses in their training and a more flexible set of prerequisites for certification. By no means is it suggested, to repeat an earlier point, that all art teachers in the schools are creative duds and malleable white-collar classroom workers. There are significant numbers of serious, competent, and inventive teachers of art in the schools, teachers who honestly value the experience of art and will not compromise the values they discern in art. Yet we need and can have many more enthusiastic, and indeed inspiring, teachers of art in the schools if art education is presented more as a career of substance and unfolding process rather than one of systematized methodologies and administrative procedures. At the very least, the interlocked limitations of certification and art teacher training tend to confuse, yet mutually exclude at times, various issues of art and education. The relationship between the two needs to be open, challenging, and pegged at a high level of excellence. It tends now to be codified, given to mediocrity, and each suspicious aspect surreptitiously, if not openly, cancels out the other.

Given such spongy background conditions, school art

programs are often cast into academic molds. They are bureaucratized unconsciously as approved "fun and games," taught by bona fide, certified individuals in scheduled curricular slots. Even in the best of situations one cannot always disregard the externally rather than the personally authenticated nature of school art programs and the vested propriety of the art education establishment, locally or nationally. Perhaps this is unescapable in the very nature of an educational system committed to an extensive cultural range of education yet disseminated on a mass scale. By its very nature, it may be almost impossible to humanize the regulatory influences demanded by complex, widespread education and exceedingly large numbers of "clients," the entire caboodle subject to paradoxical egalitarian officialism and manufactured materially affluent forces. In many ways, art teachers necessarily "bucking a system" are to be commended for their always valiant attempts to establish a climate within which artistic growth can flourish. To involve students in the mysterious challenges, the spiritual concerns, and sometimes demanding delights of art despite contrary influences is no easy task. Conceivably, the one personal trap they need to avoid is the encompassing institutionalized sentimentality or even fraudulent programming in which even the best intentions may be enveloped. The teacher's own sense of responsibility, his own existential and inner vision should serve as the criterion for attitude and action.

Here too with personnel, the extra-school art programs may suffer from similar confusions and uncertainties. Inappropriate teaching in extra-school art programs may come about from utilizing teachers who lack certification and particularized pedagogical training. However, this is probably a minimal situation that a proliferating number of programs could not avoid to some degree. The teaching personnel in extra-school art programs are commonly noncertified individuals, artists (professional and otherwise), docents, occasionally even dangling art historians. There are also highly interested adults who possess a "flair" for art. The possibility exists of a dilettantish approach with such persons. We may quite rightfully look with a jaundiced eye upon the last group though it is possible to encounter some wonderful and conspicuously sensitive art teachers among them. A number of regular certified teachers occasionally moonlight in extra-school art programs as well.

The point is that, with few exceptions, extra-school art programs do not require or demand certified teaching personnel. A fuller range of individual artistic and educational background characterizes the extra-school art program teaching personnel. As has been intimated, this more permissive acceptance may have an occasional deleterious consequence. But it may also be educationally beneficial and artistically wholesome. Active artists earnestly engaged in their own work, or people trained in a relatively rigorous scholarship as art historians usually undergo, become available. Their enthusiasm for their own work, their relative sophistication, developed insightfulness and skills, the inherent integrity of their attitudes and commitments, and their distinguishing creative verve uniquely honed, are all rather positive assets that may be a natural condition of their teaching. Thus the extra-school art programs are likely to be impressively shaped, not so much by a certified or standardized methodology, but by the passions and idiosyncrasies of an artistically committed or critically productive individual. Conceivably, "amateur" teaching personnel can also effect an inherently enthusiastic atmosphere and a more appropriately creative responsiveness from students. Particularly, today with an emphasis upon community identity and grass-roots involvement, there is a verve of expressiveness in local neighborhoods and a heightened significance to the work produced. There is also, however, within such a context the utilization of art in an instrumental manner; it becomes a tool of propaganda. This may be serving liberal social ends, but it may not encourage any legitimate aesthetic sensitivity on an individual level. In any case, extra-school art programs afford artistically value-oriented opportunities for teaching involvements not normally found in schools. It opens the way for visionary influences and the transforming qualities of practicing artists to touch directly and perhaps inspire the lives of students.

As for the varying nature of the student bodies, it may be said simply that in regular schools the students are involuntarily enrolled, whereas the opposite is most often true, for extra-school patterns. Below the secondary level, students are generally assigned to their areas of study, art as well as all the other subjects. This does not suggest because of the imposed scheduling that students resent being in an art class in school. Quite the contrary. The art period is generally the most popular period of a school day. Yet, there are negative considerations that flow from involuntary scheduling of art. Occasionally, there are students who simply reject art activities or feel uncomfortable in an art class. It is somewhat self-defeating to force an arbitrary compliance of activity upon such youngsters. More important, another arbitrary condition is imposed upon students in school—that of schematic time, or the scheduling of the art "period." Given the varying psychological contexts and the expressive independence required for legitimate art experiences, it may be disturbing or inhibiting to creative efforts to have to be at an appointed place at an appointed time that has been externally decreed. Expressive potential cannot be mechanically regulated or capriciously motivated. It requires certain freedoms and flexible responsiveness to contingency situations, which are not normally amenable to block-planning. The discipline required in art is not of a regularized nature. Rather, it functions as the harnessing of individual energies at the most uniquely appropriate psychological moment. Such moments are much more likely to function randomly than to be activated by the pushing of a scheduling button. Of course, extra-school programs are subject to time limitations too. However, these limitations usually are much looser, subject to modification as necessity arises. There need not be a strict adherence to periods and bells.

There may also be an irrelevant and unnecessarily coercive note in an educational philosophy that insists upon an extended art experience for all school children. This insistence upon art for every child subject only to its support by fat monies is simply an ideological truism. However, it may not be a true reflection of either social patterns or of the aspirations and personal needs of each and every student. Nor need it be an inviolate article of cultural faith though the unquestioned efficacy of the educative processes. This paper is not the place to argue the pros and cons of curricular democracy in art. Though it may be noted that more than one serious critic of American culture looks with skepticism upon the influences of mass taste and democratic participation in the arts. It is even suggested by one critic that no art activities in school may be a more positive condition for the growth of individual artistic insight and values than mediocre or contradictory programs. Nevertheless, more than an arbitrary democratic note is struck in the insistence upon broad inclusive opportunities to become involved in art. What was once the domain of the aristocrat and of highly cultivated sensibilities can now become an area of rewarding experience for everyone. The sense of such a belief respects the innate worth of each individual. It suggests that the schools, at least, offer the means of cultivation toward artistic expressiveness and responsiveness. However, the corollary remains that the individual's worth and his potential is predicated upon personal responsibility and growth. The school cannot circumvent the necessary individual work and involvement that stimulates learning and creates a qualitative sensibility. The cultivation of one's imagination and perceptions is still a requisite for aesthetic insights.

Empirically, the extra-school art program may reinforce such a sense of individual responsibility and personal involvement. The students that are enrolled in such programs are generally present on a voluntary basis. They have demonstrated interest in art and have acted upon such interests. Of course, some students attend extra-school art programs because of a variety of extrinsic reasons as well; there may be social satisfactions, peer pressures or those of the home, and sometimes the attendance is out of sheer boredom. Nevertheless, the majority of students attending after-school art programs do so because this is what they want to do.

The resulting atmosphere of the center or museum program tends to be lively and productive. There is a mutual reinforcement of desires and conditions because a motivating force is intrinsically and consistently generated and maintained. Despite the lack of a graded, systematic curriculum, or perhaps because of such a lack, an open-ended quality of activity is a characteristic aspect. There is present in a typical extra-school program a spontaneous climate of making and doing, of expressive absorption and satisfaction. The freedom of attendance, working periods, and of creative verve as well as the freedom from abstract, academically imposed constraints of curricular sequence or scheduling are fundamental aspects of pedagogical structure of which all educators should be aware. There is an obvious need to reassess the current patterns of school organization, at least in relationship to the teaching of art. A more flexible, loosely structured approach is indicated as to who shall be exposed to art education and when.

It has not been the intent of this paper to pit school and nonschool art programs against one another—to present them as adversaries. That would be both foolish and irresponsible. However, what has been implied is an encouragement toward mutual examination. Since the schools are official state institutions far more influential and much larger in size and in sources of support they become the obvious target of criticism. For these same reasons, the schools have a much greater responsibility for critical self-examination. This is especially so today when many educational "failings" are becoming apparent even if such "failings" are more the result of changing cultural mores and newly awakened political pressures. The need for intelligent change remains no matter where the reasons for change originate.

Conceivably, in matters of art education the schools can divest themselves of any jurisdictional prerogatives they may cherish. They can and should reach out to those external institutions that are imaginatively and enthusiastically involved with art programs. In so doing they would establish a healthy interaction among arts educators that would be mutually beneficial. Such encounters and exchanges would encourage and expand a lively interest in art within the context of education. The schools would not only be discharging their responsibilities to students to educate in the most desirable manner; they would also be contributing to an enhanced quality of life—a central concern that is becoming evident for the decade of the seventies.

TWO INTERVIEWS: INTERVIEW WITH
AN ANONYMOUS ARTIST *
AND INTERVIEW WITH SCOTT FREE

Cindy Nemser

. . . .

Cindy Nemser takes a few pokes at art world stereotypes in these unlikely interviews with artists—one of whom is anonymous, won't show his work, and makes authentic "non-art." Primarily, Conceptual and anti-art artists are the subjects of Ms. Nemser's joking.

The author is a regular contributor to Arts Magazine, *and has written for* Artforum, Art in America, *and* The Art Journal.

. . . .

INTERVIEW WITH AN ANONYMOUS ARTIST

This interview takes place on a stretch of barren marshland somewhere on the coast of southern New Jersey.

INTERVIEWER (*looking around suspiciously*): Well, I think we will be safe here. Now, tell me, who are you? Where can your work be seen?

* Reprinted from *Art Education* (January, 1970).

Cindy Nemser

ARTIST: Please—no names, no places. I speak for a group of artists whose identity must remain a secret. Their art is disguised as non-art. To reveal its location would destroy its validity.

INTERVIEWER: You mean your group never shows at museums or art galleries?

ARTIST: Absolutely not! We believe that art viewed in the context of commercial art galleries or publicity-ridden museums is doomed to be experienced in a narrow, inhibiting manner. You come to those places primed for an aesthetic experience. You feel gypped if you don't have it, and, what's more, it better be the right kind of aesthetic experience.

INTERVIEWER: How could you do away with this unbearably artificial situation?

ARTIST: There is only one solution. We must get art out of the galleries and museums. Artists must confront the public on the city streets, the town squares, and the local countryside. Robert Rauschenberg said he was acting in the gap between art and life. We believe that that gap should be eliminated entirely. We want to make an art that resembles life so closely that the viewer will be unable to disentangle the one from the other. Then he can respond to art without any preconceived aesthetic assumptions.

INTERVIEWER: Then you would not let your viewers know that they are having an aesthetic experience?

ARTIST: Certainly not. In fact we deliberately withhold all clues that might reveal what we are up to.

INTERVIEWER: But don't you believe that one gains more out of an aesthetic experience by knowing something about its aims and intentions?

ARTIST: Not necessarily. By being able to respond to a seemingly natural phenomenon or situation, the viewer can react in a completely natural manner. He could never achieve much spontaneity if he knew he was viewing "art." Through anonymous art the passive spectator is transformed into an active participant. He becomes deeply involved as a total being, bringing to the experience all his own deep-seated emotions and ideas. At last he can react with genuine feeling, not the artificial simulated response he has been taught to associate with a work of art.

INTERVIEWER: If your productions are so lifelike, how can you call them art at all?

ARTIST: Let me assure you. Our creations may imitate life, but they are as carefully conceived, constructed, and executed as any traditionally accepted art form.

INTERVIEWER: What kind of art experience do you offer?

ARTIST: Here are examples of the works of three artists who choose to remain anonymous. Artist #1 works on natural scenery. He adds globs of Jello to the other assortments of flotsam thrown up on the seashore. He festoons the beaches with bright yellow ribbons, and stains the ice with vivid Day-Glo paints. The waters of the ocean nearest the shore turn bright green after he saturates them with vats of green paint.

INTERVIEWER: He sounds like a mod Queen Mab—a landscape painter in the most literal sense of the word. What about Artist #2?

ARTIST: He also plays pranks on the natural order. Streams flow upward because of his manipulations. By his ministrations, carved-out hollows of sand, resembling the work of some amphibian creature, appear on beaches.

INTERVIEWER (*pointing to the right*): You mean that large hole over there might be his doing?

ARTIST: It's possible—but I don't think he knows this territory.

INTERVIEWER: Does anonymous Artist #3 redecorate scenery, too?

ARTIST: No. He prefers to do his aesthetic acts in a man-made setting, and incorporate people as well as objects into his events.

INTERVIEWER: He sounds like a Happener.

ARTIST: He isn't. There's none of that self-conscious posturing in his activities. His most recent creation consisted of a brilliant series of consecutive actions. First, he arrived in a small Midwestern town passing himself off as a research soil sampler. He took various specimens from the locale and departed. A month later, dressed in artist's regalia, he returned in a small panel truck that contained some undisclosed objects. In the backyard of a rented house, this eccentric intruder erected a tent that he kept brightly lit day and night. His erratic behavior caused a minor sensation among the local populace. Peeping Toms came from everywhere to check up on these strange goings-on. Then as suddenly as he appeared, the mysterious interloper departed. Within the confines of the tent, the perplexed townspeople discovered five apple seedlings, nurtured by the earth samples of their native soil.

INTERVIEWER: A nice performance indeed, but I'm rather disappointed. After all, messing up—I mean *manipulating*—the scenery and mystifying the man on the street are not exactly innovations in this day and age. Famous and not so famous artists are doing similar things right at this moment. To name a few: Oldenburg, Heizer, Oppenheim, Kaltenbach, and Long have already invaded the urban complex, the town square, and the more remote backwoods regions.

ARTIST: True, these people are making an effort to reach out and communicate with the general public. Nevertheless, they are simply making futile gestures.

INTERVIEWER: What brings you to that conclusion?

ARTIST: They are afraid to go all the way toward merging art with life. Falling back on the traditional gallery or museum exhibition, they inevitably mark their efforts as art, not life. Their activities and creations may look and sound unorthodox, but their means of presentation are depressingly conventional. The press releases go out, the opening occurs, and the critics and reviewers arrive and dutifully record. Why, only recently, a whole plane-load of artists, critics, and coordinators were carted up to the Cornell University museum to view the "natural phenomena" constructed by well-publicized artists. The critics did what was expected of them, and the first description of their venture into the hinterlands has already appeared in detail in John Perreault's column in *The Village Voice*.

INTERVIEWER: What about artists who do not show in galleries or museums?

ARTIST: Just by identifying themselves they mar the spontaneity of the viewer's experience of their art.

INTERVIEWER: But without galleries and museums to promote them, how do these artists become known to the public?

ARTIST: They form groups and issue statements in esoteric art magazines. Then the media get to them, and their names appear in major newspapers and periodicals, not to mention appearances on the *Today* show.

INTERVIEWER: Well, if you wish to dispense with all the claptrap and publicity seeking, why are you telling me about your ideas and intentions?

ARTIST: My dear, we as artists must acknowledge our debt to the past as well as our responsibility to the future. It is our duty to art to assume both obligations by informing a small art-oriented group about the actual motivation behind our activities.

INTERVIEWER: I guess the art historians will place you between the earth movers and art de-materializers, acknowledging, of course, your debt to the abstract conceptualists, and documenting your influence on the erotic perceptionists.

ARTIST: Yes. It will be annoying to be categorized along with the rest, but we will have had the satisfaction of having done right by past and future generations.

INTERVIEWER: Your stoicism is admirable, but don't you think that you are being just a little elitist by keeping your secret confined to a small "in" group?

ARTIST: Heavens, no! Don't you see that those who don't know that they are involved in an art experience are the real beneficiaries?

INTERVIEWER: And you really think you can remain unknown?

ARTIST (*gives a sigh of resignation*): We'll try our darndest, but I suppose the media will get to us eventually, and then everyone will know about anonymous art.

INTERVIEWER: I can just see it. People will be constantly on the alert. They will begin to expect a Happening on every street corner and an artist in every backyard.

ARTIST: Say, it might not be bad at that! Imagine, we as artists will influence man's everyday living consciousness. We will have altered his whole way of perceiving his environment. Certainly loss of anonymity is a small sacrifice for bringing about this idyllic situation.

INTERVIEWER: Your selflessness is overwhelming. I don't know how to thank you for all the time and trouble you've taken to give me this interview. It took great moral courage on your part to reveal yourself to me.

ARTIST: A man must do what he has to—but, please, do me one favor.

INTERVIEWER: Anything you ask.

ARTIST: Please get this interview down on paper before your next deadline. Anonymous art has remained unknown for too long—and one more thing.

INTERVIEWER: Yes.

ARTIST: When the dreadful moment arrives for us to step forth and disclose our identities, make sure you spell my name right.

INTERVIEW WITH SCOTT FREE

The interview takes place in the loft of Scott Free, the long-haired, tie-dyed, bug-eyed, ingenuous generator of open-option art. Stumbling into his chinos, Scott motions me into a chair, offers me black coffee in one of his famous penis-handled mugs, and shoves a bowl strewn with ceramic feces at me, which, I assume, correctly, is to be used as an ashtray. Then turning toward me with an innocent boyish grin, he indicates that he is ready to be interviewed.

Q.: What kind of work do you do?

A.: Well, I don't like to put my work into any kind of a category—like art should be free to be anything that it is.

Q.: Does open-option art only encompass Conceptual art or does it include objects as well?

A.: You sure want to pin a guy down—well all art is conceptual, even if it becomes objectified, so I guess you could call me a Conceptual artist who makes objects. I feel free to do both.

Q.: Could you describe some of the works that you have done in the Conceptual line?

A.: I write a lot of letters. Anytime I get an idea about anything I write it down and send it out to someone I think it might interest.

Q.: Is that all you do?

A.: Well I'm not the sort of person who is required to follow things through as that would take a great deal of time and effort and impinge on my freedom.

Q.: What happens after you send out the letters?

A.: I really don't know, I never got back any answers, but I don't mind since I feel free to imagine any kind of responses I like.

Q.: You mean you don't have to deal with reality at all?

A.: Right, I can make up my own reality, and that makes me a free and happy artist.

Q.: So once the idea is sent off, that's all there is to it?

A.: Well, I do document it and keep a careful record of my suggestions. After all, you never know who might say they thought of the idea first.

Q.: Would that bother you, if another person got credit for an idea that you thought up?

A.: To be perfectly honest, it used to bother me a lot. But now I've worked my way out of that hang-up.

Q.: Excuse me, Mr. Free, but did you say *you* had hang-ups?

A.: Oh, yes, all sorts of hang-ups. For instance, I used to be all hung-up about my appearance, my sex, my originality, my love life, my intelligence, my . . .

Q.: Excuse me, but how did you work your way out of the "who got the idea first" hang-up?

A.: Oh, that was easy, no matter what ideas I stole . . . I mean utilized, I said it was my idea first, because saying it was my idea first was my artwork. I called it utilization art.

Q.: So, no matter who comes up with an idea first, ultimately it becomes yours. Yes, that does away with the problem of originality. Did you realize from the beginning that you were doing utilization art?

A.: No, but I had collected an awful lot of other people's ideas and I had to think of some way to get credit for them. If I had to sit around thinking up my own ideas, it would be a terrible encroachment on my free time.

Q.: What other hang-ups have you worked your way out of?

A.: Well, I never trusted people. I always thought they were trying to screw me. So I would try to screw them first and then I would feel guilty about it.

Q.: How did you get out of that one through your art?

A.: Well, now I make my art out of screwing people

and since it's a work of art, objectified, out in the open, I no longer hate myself for it. I can live with it. I'm free!

Q.: What about the people you've screwed?

A.: They can make a work of art out of it too and then think how lucky they are to have acquired a work of art free of charge.

Q.: What about your love life hang-up? How did you get free from that?

A.: I used to be afraid to tell my wife about making it with other chicks, now . . .

Q.: I know you make an artwork out of it and you tell her about it with confidence everytime.

A.: Right, in fact I'm ready for that kind of artwork any time. I call that my collaborative art—(*looking at me with a shy smile*) interested in collaborating?

Q.: Let's get on to non-hang-up art. What other kinds of art do you do?

A.: I make open-option art.

Q.: What do you mean by that?

A.: Art that is known as art is so closed, so circumscribed, so lacking in freedom. Once something is known as art, people react to it in such a set, predetermined way. I make art that no one knows is art.

Q.: How do you do that?

A.: I throw garbage on the street, I chalk up the walls of public rest rooms, I mutilate public telephones, I follow people when they aren't looking, I give out grass.

Q.: You sound more like a public nuisance than an artist.

A.: But that's the whole idea, to keep people's minds open, to make them react in a real way, to keep them from having a strictly closed-circuit everyday art experience.

Q.: But those activities are dangerous, you might end up in jail.

A.: I know it's a risky business, but if one is to make art that is really free, one must be prepared to take chances.

Q.: I really envy you your courage. When this interview is published, it will be an inspiration to all those uptight souls who are secretly yearning to plunge into a life of freedom like yours.

A.: You are going to *publish* this interview?

Q.: Of course, didn't I tell you that before we started this discussion?

A.: Oh, I thought we were just having a little heart-to-heart talk, but if it's for publication, you have to leave some things out.

Q.: Such as?

A.: Well, let me see—some people might not let me steal—I mean utilize their ideas if I tell them that I do it, so leave that out; and people never enjoyed getting screwed even as an artwork, so forget about that too.

Q.: Anything else?

A.: Well, my wife would kill me if she knew about my collaboration pieces, so we'd better not mention them— and since littering, damaging public property, and pushing grass are illegal, you'd better not mention any of those things either. Otherwise, feel free to quote anything I've said from beginning to end.

Q.: Well thanks a lot, it's not everyday I meet a free spirit like you.

Part Five

. . . .

EXPERIMENT
AND
PROPOSAL

James Sullivan

PERCEPTARIUM

James Sullivan

. . . .

The college art department should lead the way in inventing and promoting new learning patterns and educational goals, according to James Sullivan. Instead, the majority of art departments have become as compartment-alized, insulated, and rigid as other academic disciplines.

In this essay Sullivan notes that college art departments by perpetuating "only the safe and traditional and by adopting the mechanisms of academia . . . have missed the opportunity to revolutionize learning in gen-eral." In fact, young artists leaving the univer-sities should have "the conceptual equipment to create roles for themselves for which at the moment we have few descriptions and even fewer labels."

Sullivan is not optimistic about the future for art schools, or for university education in general. He writes: "After recoiling from stu-dents' demands for innovation, the major efforts of many schools now seem to be de-voted to recuperating from those demands and getting things back to where they were." And, instead of devoting energy to creating a climate that would give the student the opportunity to think, they expend enormous energy ". . . in lecture and studio courses to the transmitting of information that any university student should be able to acquire on his own, given intelligent guidance."

The author calls for the development of new learning environments to aid ". . . education's shift from baby-sitting to independent learning activity," and he advocates construction of a Perceptarium that would "serve as a visual center devoted to the creation . . . of alternative futures." Not merely "another magic lantern or sensorium" the Perceptarium would ". . . receive and structure stimulation from all the various nerve pathways on the campus as well as to illustrate knowledge past and present into projections for the future."

The operational designs and architectural plans for the Perceptarium are highly original, yet rational and, perhaps, workable. However, without "a fundamental realignment of higher education's spirit and methods, a Perceptarium would become another assemblage of hardware . . ." or, in other words, a wild-goose chase.

James Sullivan teaches in the School of Art at the University of Southern Illinois. Once he encouraged his art history students to build birdhouses instead of writing a term paper.

. . . .

"Vision is the necessary antecedent to control and direction."—ALFRED NORTH WHITEHEAD

"What you see is what you get"—FLIP WILSON

The purpose of this essay is to suggest ways by which the university and the art department can actualize, through vision, alternatives to the problems that affect the quality of all our lives. While the major concern rests with the concept of a Perceptarium as an environment that visually synergizes information past and present into potential futures, a number of attendant observations upon the quality and direction of higher education are also in order. . For without a fundamental realignment of higher education's spirit and methods, a Perceptarium would become another assemblage of hardware gone to the cause of the magic lantern.

Our society, not unlike the tombstone which reads, "All dressed up and no place to go," has resources capable of alleviating much of today's suffering. Yet being effective in the here and now seems to be beyond our capacity. Like the motion of an electron whose evasiveness defies our most sophisticated attempts to pin it down, we find it difficult to know exactly where things are at. The electron offers a microcosmic parody of the dilemma confronting education today. Information bombards us from every conceivable direction. In various forms of disconnectedness it urges us to give it form and purpose while simultaneously evading our ability to understand and control it. And all the while, and in the midst of it all, we are still *preparing* young people for something they will do in the future. Education's opposite and equal reaction to the pace of things is procrastination. Being not where it's at and having no place to go has become the second-largest industry in the United States.

Being modern is a perennial problem. What makes that historical dilemma different at this point in our evolution, is the *necessity* to be creatively involved in the here and now. It is an imperative that demands new adaptations lest we experience the extinction that awaits any species whose primary energy is devoted to elaborating upon inertia.

To control the complexity that moves us willy-nilly along we have to learn new adaptive principles that will see us, like Huxley's multiple amphibians, capable of "living simultaneously in a number of incommensurable worlds at once." Thus the opportunity arises for the contemporary artist to function as an ultra-amphibian, free of hierarchies of state, myth, medium, or his own lately overdeveloped ego. If he assumes the responsibility this new freedom invites he will be a very ancient shaman in a modern amphibian's disguise. In effect, the primitive artist of the future.

Discovering aesthetic solutions to today's formlessness may be the most exciting territory that a student-artist can explore. Creating new roles for aspiring artists will require a complete overhaul of our institutions of learning and a breed of students whose demands for freedom and autonomy will be matched by their willingness to accept a new and multidimensional responsibility. That is currently not the case. More often than not, those students who clamor most loudly for freedom have no idea what to do with it. Nor do they have the desire to invest the energy that is always the price of innovation. The inertia of the institutions is too frequently complemented by the apathy of its students. These combine to create, across the country, a profusion of middle-class, ivy-covered islands of Cythera.

Simply prolonging the adolescent state while preparing students for some obscure future role denies the very obvious observation that these people *are* alive! An education aimed toward contemporary re-creation through independence, responsibility, and imagination will certainly stir the sleeping giant. Yet even if doomed to failure, the attempt would be infinitely more interesting and enjoyable than the foolish consistency of today's training programs. With a restoration of purpose and vision in education the suggestion arises that most of the courses one finds in catalogues are packages of concepts and information that most students should be able to learn given the right environment and guidance, on their own. This would clear the path to the development of new curricula stressing the creative application of knowledge to situations that exist now and to the production of alternative human environments that will need to exist in any future of quality. Some interesting by-products might be a lessening of the mediocrity that characterizes much of higher education today; the development of new standards of excellence that would restore meaning to the proliferation of degrees in higher learning; a resurrection of genuine scholarship and a return to the fundamental adventure and religiosity of learning.

OBSERVATIONS ON THE CONTEMPORARY ART ACADEMY

Using knowledge actively and independently infers an elasticity in the learning environment that of all places on campus should be apparent in departments of art. Yet for the main, they persist in a historically pinched definition of tradition. One which contributes to the notion of the artist as alien; a lonely maker of objects disenfranchised from and misunderstood by his society. In negotiating their place in the academic sun, art departments capitulated to the inertia in which most levels of education today is immersed. By perpetuating only the safe and traditional and by adopting the mechanisms of academia, art schools have missed the opportunity to revolutionize learning in general.

The experience of the undergraduate in art consists of a series of academic Newtonian steps wherein instructors deal with those things with which they are most comfortable: namely, those forms of art that were quite fully developed in the sixteenth century. When this artistic sequential hurdling is coupled with the current shotgun approach to a liberal education in the general studies area, one understands why so many graduate students in art simply want to be left alone. By democratizing the experiential steps by which one arrived at the degree objective the contemporary academy insured two results. First, that the objective and its carefully prescribed form would more than likely never be transcended and, more importantly, that the responsibility for learning, which is almost wholly the student's, was taken out of his hands and placed in the administrative grasp of institutions. In a time when social and environmental horror is the order of the day, a time when many artists everywhere are helping people, academia persists in fostering the fabrication of objects in a social and intellectual vacuum. Great civilizations have always woven tapestries that reflect, in harmony with nature, the meaning and purpose of human life. The absence today of these transcendent models, which spring from involvement with life, is obvious. With our diminishing attempts to capture fantasy and mold it into visible alternative futures we simultaneously abdicate the responsibility of effecting a renewal in the quality of contemporary life. Thus art schools have become as compartmentalized and insulated from the pathos of their times as other academic superspecialties. In the name of liberal education, art students endure a two-year mélange of disconnected course work that usually consists of unrelated introductions to various professional disciplines. Rarely are connections made between the underlying and interrelated principles operational to these various fields. Even rarer is an attempt to tread on controversial ground by relating those principles to matters of value and contemporary importance. With great relief, the art student then enters the art laboratory for the next two years, matriculates into life, and, if he doesn't attend graduate school or go through public school certification, winds up selling insurance. Like the engineering student whose information is obsolete at the moment of its attainment, or the socially myopic scientist, he pays a heavy price for the insulation that his education has provided him. Perhaps the noblest thrust of art education in America has been the attempt to convince everyone that he is an artist, that everyone has an imaginative stake in the future, that everyone needs to be involved artistically in a change in the quality of life. It is a singular irony that those most well equipped to do this have so few alternatives available to them. These observations are not intended to denigrate the professional object-making activities that are today the primary function of art departments. Yet new areas of learning that stress a correspondence between traditional artists' roles and contemporary problems are vitally needed. Young artists leaving our universities and colleges should have the conceptual equipment to create roles for themselves for which at the moment we have few descriptions and even fewer labels. It's lamentable that we continue in the illusion that we are training artists who are somehow or other different kinds of people. More than likely creation of the traditional forms will occur as they always have, in the solitude of the studio. Certainly a concern with specialization is essential. But an insulated specialization that does not punctuate the totality of things to which it is related is self-defeating. When art does not evolve out of life, it becomes sterile, a dull academic exercise. Specialization is nurtured through contrast, thus any dramatic shift in the form and priorities of art departments will not only increase the numbers of young people who will cope artistically with social and environmental problems, but will also enhance and lend vitality to efforts in the more traditional forms. Art departments can make the best of both possible worlds, that of the inherent autonomy within the "art for art's sake" concept and the need for reestablishing ancient roles in a new way for artists; that being the extension of their aesthetic sensibilities into the mainstream of life.

In summary, these two major trends, perpetuating only professional concerns and the increase in social and academic compartmentalization, combine to:

Prevent a new but very ancient union between the artist and his culture.

Squelch a new social consciousness that many art students see as an organic extension and reinforcement of their individual studio involvement.

Vitiate the image/energy of the more traditional art forms by (in the name of freedom and professionalism) encouraging their fabrication, in a social and disconnected intellectual vacuum.

Cultivate the romantic ego-mystic of the artist as a disenfranchised being living on the periphery of his culture.

Prevent individual discovery of fresh associations which emerge through experimentation and play, by academically overprescribing the steps by which a student arrives at the discovery of form.

Emphasize the exclusiveness of being an artist through an overemphasis on specialization which in turn reinforces the public notion that everyone is not an artist.

SOME CHANGES ON THE WAY TO THE PERCEPTARIUM

In *The Sleepwalkers,* Arthur Koestler observes that, "the inertia of the human mind and its resistance to innovation are most clearly demonstrated not, as one might expect, by the ignorant mass—which is easily swayed once its imagination is caught—but by the professionals with a vested interest in tradition and in the monopoly of learning. Innovation is a twofold threat to academic mediocrities; it endangers their oracular authority, and it evokes the deeper fear that their whole laboriously constructed intellectual edifice may collapse." A third threat should be added to Koestler's. Real change, not just movement, requires planning and work. With the archaic learning procedures currently used and the increasing numbers of students entering higher education, many faculties have as little opportunity to think as the students themselves. Great amounts of energy are devoted simply to getting and keeping the doors open.

New areas within art departments needn't threaten the professional interests of scholars and artists. Their development should be encouraged because the expressions of social concern by many students *are* a reality. Their desires to contribute to the quality of life are not simply sophomoric urges to be do-gooders, neither are they all fuzzy-minded little Neo-Marxists. Their concerns, a fact in which faculties should take delight, are sincere. In the sixties a gauntlet for change was thrown to the universities by the students. Few fundamental changes have been made and many indications now suggest that both are abdicating and reverting back to the comforts of a more easily defined tradition. After recoiling from students' demands for innovation, the major efforts of many schools now seem to be devoted to recuperating from those demands and getting things back to where they were. If anything, schools should be testing every conceivable method for harnessing those concerns and relating them actively to academic programs before they die (as they already appear to be doing). There's nothing more vicious in the end than the violence of a human being against those whose complicity has contributed to his own personal abdication of freedom. These student-artists are the contemporary progeny of all those ancient magic-makers and myth-revealers inhabiting historical space and time. They deserve more than academic busy-work. With refreshing frequency many students in art are asking for guidance and direction in helping them sort out and discover contributions that they might make to society at large. They are fishing around and hearteningly, for the most part, they are quite serious. They are troubled by the conflict of living in a world of decreasing human quality while creating within an environment that unconsciously enforces the concept of the disinherited artist.

All too often these students are confronted with a gamut of misunderstandings. Observations to the effect that "We have no area of Conceptual art within our department" or, "Have you thought about majoring in Design or Sociology?" Or most effective of all the various "downers," "Why don't you major in Home Economics?" (A suggestion that in the eyes of at least one major American art critic has a great deal of merit!) This concern isn't necessarily a screen for incompetence in traditional studio involvements. Hopefully it is the beginning of a movement that will contribute to centralizing in our society a concern with the qualitative aspects of life. Admitting that prophesying is difficult, especially about the future, one may feel, however, that this searching for new ways of contributing aesthetic energy into the mainstream of life is a revival of a more monumental and profound concept of artistic tradition. By obliterating even further the distinction between art and life, we may not only contribute to the spiritual and physical health of our society, but also, ironically, rediscover art in the process. For surely one of the bizarre ingredients of the contemporary tragedy is precisely the inability to distinguish between art and reality. The development of new programs in art departments addressed to these young people, however alien the idea might initially sound, is one of the most inventive tasks confronting art education today.

A necessary step toward an academic definition of new social roles for the artist will be a developing autonomy within art departments. The major responsibility for reconciling the aims of a liberal education with specialization would be the departments'. A preliminary move would be the replacement of sequential art and general studies curricula with fewer and more fully integrated experiences. The basic information relating to practically any art course can be assimilated independently by students in specially designed environments accompanied by appropriate guidelines. Upper division students could receive credit for serving as tutors for freshmen and sophomore students and graduate students would, in turn, receive credit for helping undergraduates. Students then would enter small seminars where the information, independently assimilated, would be used as an active research tool into more problematical areas of investigation. It is pathetic that so much time and energy is devoted in lecture and studio courses to the transmitting of information that any university student should be able to acquire on his own, given intelligent guidance. This would result in a new freedom and independence for students, and it would provide a basis for later conscionable evaluations of a student's will and capacity. It would also provide him with an opportunity conspicuously absent in the current whirlwind of course requirements: the opportunity to think, to work at his own pace, and to find out if he is doing what he really wants to do. Moreover, it would shift the professor's role to that of a guide and companion in exploration rather than a mere transmitter of information and technique. The general education aspects of a student's learning should involve a few courses taught by generalists, men and women who, while having expertise in an area of art, are capable of relating art to the sum knowledge and experience of man. Their principal task would be to help the student integrate his own developing set of concerns within the larger configuration of the scientific, humanistic, and natural history of life.

These changes could help create new and needed areas of concern and scholarship within art departments, stimulate the traditional areas, and would more closely approximate the aims of a liberal education. Most importantly, however, by broadening, and at the same time integrating the student's special area within the sum of human experience, we would be providing young artists with at least the basic equipment to carve out new and meaningful roles in society.

THE PERCEPTARIUM

One corollary to education's shift from baby-sitting to independent learning activity will be the development of new learning environments. Technology, though it might repulse the nouveaux Orientalists among us, will be an essential ingredient in the creation of new perceptual centers. Persisting in a Cartesian belief that technology is one thing and man another offers little hope for escaping this fifth apocalyptic rider. Technology is a human extension of man into and upon the environment, and as such it is a potential artistic medium inherently no better or worse than oil, plaster, or clay. Through technology the function of the Perceptarium becomes an ancient one, that of making the invisible visible. An artistic harnessing of technology through the collaborative creative effort of many disciplines could create what would, in effect, be a new cultural compass. Thus culture itself, pre-envisioned in the minds of the people who are about to create it, is regarded as a necessary imaginative act for the sake of survival. To avoid mechanistic or totalitarian utopias we need to know what the potential alternatives are, and we desperately need a new language that will convey those alternatives to everyone. We need feedback from the extensions we use to mold the social and natural environment. Art, in addition to embodying the interpretations of a culture, has always supplied the empathetic response that reinforces the survival value of a culture's vision. The Perceptarium would serve as a visual center devoted to the creation, through multidisciplinary efforts guided by artists, of alternative futures. Far from being another magic lantern or sensorium, it would be an environment existing on campus in much the same way as the cyton, the body of a nerve cell, operates in the human brain. Its function would be to receive and structure stimulation from all the various nerve pathways on the campus, as well as to develop knowledge, past and present, into projections for the future. As an architectural entity the Perceptarium would be centrally located, like a Gothic cathedral, at the hub of a university's activity. A contemporary version of the de-materialization of form that expressed the mystical longing of Gothic cathedrals, it would be the architectural antithesis of today's ubiquitous bureaucratic structures. The external form of the Perceptarium would be in constant movement. It would present a metamorphic interplay of organic and geometric, solid and transitory elements. These would evoke perceptions of de-materializing form within a context of dynamic equilibrium. One's first visual contact with the Perceptarium would be the apprehension of an architectural archetype that orders moving parts within a rational whole. In this respect the outer form would be a metabolic extension of the structure's internal function: namely, fresh comprehensions experienced through new frames of perceptual reference. The outer form itself would testify to notions of adaptability and change. Through a movement of its components into varying patterns and configurations, dismemberments and biomorphic readjustments, the Perceptarium would perform its own kinetic, architectural dance of life. Its changing presence would affirm and celebrate the notion of discovery and daily creative renewal. The potential for challenging peoples' preconceived notions about what buildings are and how they have to be built would in itself have important impact as a learning experience. Internally, the Perceptarium would consist of audio-visual ecosystems inviting the participation of groups and individuals. These perceptual environments would make visible the psychophysical dynamics of matter—living and inert, micro- and macrocosmic. Presented holistically, through the use of technology as an art medium, would be spectra of sensory experience. These would range from the presentation of raw perceptual data to images of alternate eco-aesthetic systems ranging from the individual to spatial levels. The Perceptarium would also illustrate the history of the Earth and man: the unfolding of creation, the evolution of life and culture, together with leaps into the future of man and nature. Finding out where we have been, in terms of our experience as a species, is a necessary prelude to understanding why we have the problems we do. It is also the indispensable corollary to conjecturing about the future, and that is a necessary exercise for effecting change now. The Perceptarium as a symbol and as a visual learning environment would translate into nonlinear models the information and implications that float about a campus: those bits and pieces of knowledge and understanding that seem to promise synthesis but that continually evade our hopeful grasp. Tending this visual "chapel of perceptions," like gardeners, would be an array of artists, scientists, technicians, students, and a permanent staff. Their aesthetic play would be directed toward translating the technological expansion of human perception into metaphors that the species has always required as it evolves through and adapts to change. From their efforts would evolve concrete proposals to the many socio-environmental problems that we currently face. As the participants within this ongoing research and creative laboratory change and as new technological innovations are developed, new problems uncovered, the form and the content of the Perceptarium would metamorphose accordingly. This capacity for change, adaptation, and growth would be an integral part of the Perceptarium's design. Such a structural- environment, devoted to the creation of solutions through perceptual metaphors, would have to be the product of a multidisciplinary effort without precedent. That, however, is precisely what the contemporary condition demands if it is to have a future.

SUMMARY

The capacity to cope with and control the hallucinogenic experience of contemporary reality may well be a survival test imposed upon the human mind by evolution. Can we begin to realize the use of those most-untapped resources of the mind without challenging them? Today's media, coupled with our linear and over-verbalized approach to education, are inadequate methods for synthesizing the enormous amount of knowledge and information engulfing us. The crux of the matter is the fact that we really don't know what "we know" means. In order to interpret the mountains of technical and social information now available into intelligible configurations we need a new language. Its new verb tense will be a visualization of the creative process itself. Computer experts, neurologists, and biotechnicians are already taking over the anthropologists' role. They may be evolving systems for the life of human beings that would strike an artist as being singularly repugnant. In addition to providing glimpses into the future, the Perceptarium would also function as an alert center where theories of social organization are projected into their concrete visual embodiments. If freedom, the prerequisite to individual dignity, becomes the aim of an enlightened culture, then everyone must choose the kind of pattern controlling his destiny. To realize this self-determination everyone must understand the language, a language that fulfills the urge toward synoptic perceptual comprehension that young people exhibit today and that is not being fulfilled by the media. Will the artist form this language by using technology to explain it and its implications for the quality of life? There is so much invisible happening that results in horror and inequity. Who will give this language form so choices can be made? If there is a new art, it will be a new language that will communicate alternatives to free people. In the creation of visual alternatives for the future we may find the will, through aspiration, to take care of the intermediate tasks.

If the university is a repository for man's past attempts at humanizing himself, then every student who leaves it ought to take with him a well-developed consciousness of time. Rather than an insulated cultural outlook or the sense of impotence that our fragmented learning experience provides, students should leave with some faith that the apparent chaos we now experience is a temporary confusion within a more comprehensible whole. In essence, it is the faith that he or she can do something about it. Our own cultural myopia binds us so tightly that resistance to innovation feeds upon itself and becomes a highly developed and protective security system. One way we can step outside ourselves is by absorbing the insight of the past and translating it through our concerns for the present into aspirational models for the future. Either we are all artists, the conscious formations of our imaginative extensions into an immeasurably complex reality, or we are captives not of some divine pre-determinism, but the victims of our own impoverished vision. Toward this end the Perceptarium exists as the revelator of collective vision and as a cultural beacon. In essence, our contemporary oracle, a divinator to which everyone makes his artistic contribution.

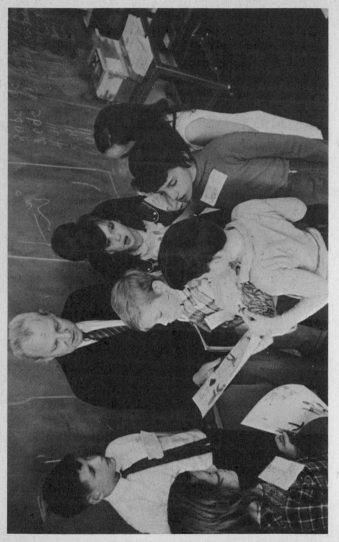

Al Hurwitz the way he likes it—surrounded by kids.

EXPERIMENT IN INTERMEDIA *

Al Hurwitz

. . . .

The unique educational experiment involving interrelated activities in several media that is described here probably would not work in most educational situations. However its impracticability is just one of the interesting things about it: it is not necessarily a liability. Does not R. Buckminster Fuller inform us that " . . . every time you make an experiment you learn more; quite literally, YOU CAN NOT LEARN LESS." (Approaching the Benign Environment [*New York: Collier, 1970*]), *p. 75.*

What is of special interest is the author's conclusion—namely that "the intermedia movement is an urban phenomenon, serving as a fresh vehicle of expression for the frustrations of race, war, and social imbalance of all kinds."

Though the goal of the experiment was a fairly conventional one, vaguely stated as ". . . the hope that we may begin to deal with some positive aspects of the human condition," the author accepts no simple answers. He warns "No one should embark on any role

* Reprinted from *Art Education* (March, 1970).

*in intermedia if he is unsympathetic to the
apparently antisocial conduct of youth . . ."*

*Approaches to intermedia programs are a
dime a dozen. Probably nobody will ever
come up with a format that can be applied
successfully in various situations. The very
idea of intermedia implies a temporary condition that, although seemingly leading to de-
specialization, is nevertheless closely linked to
new developments in art. Therefore it is the
sort of phenomenon that must be current and
spontaneous. For this reason Hurwitz warns:
"Avoid intermedia if you see yourself as an
'authority' figure or if you don't know how to
listen. Don't get involved . . . if you need a
blueprint for the future."*

*Al Hurwitz, coordinator of the arts for the
Newton Public Schools (Massachusetts), is an
associate in Education at the Harvard Graduate School of Education. He is editor of* Programs of Promise: Art in the Schools *(New
York: Harcourt Brace Jovanovich, 1972).*

. . . .

This is an account of what happened in a unique summer school that was located on a mountain just outside
the village of Cummington, Massachusetts, on the
edge of the Berkshires. The school, if one may describe
it as such, was noteworthy, not only for the content with
which it dealt, but for its loose, freewheeling structure.
There were no fixed schedules (other than those imposed by the cook), nor were there, indeed, any rules
that might in any way restrict the actions of its thirty-
odd participants. Staff and students wanted it this way,
and the directors felt that in this particular situation,

a strong element of faith was required if the group was to get at the kinds of connections the school was designed to create. A glance at the contents of the brochure will provide some idea of what Cummington offered those who would attend:

> . . . for students and teachers who feel a need to go beyond the conventional boundaries of the visual and performing arts. Cummington has planned a milieu wherein sculpture may merge with movement, film with dance; where drama may engage the audience with a repertoire of sensual stimuli; and where traditional barriers between the arts dissolve in the process of redefinition . . . Cummington will provide an opportunity for students to work in combines, happenings, or assemblages; to investigate a range of media technology to include light, sound, and the projected image; indeed, the human form and personality itself may become a component of the enactment through choreography, dramatic games, improvisations, and prepared scenes. Cummington will provide a fluid situation where a student may one week investigate painted sculpture and the next discover himself participating in a classmate's complex arrangement of a multimedia art form. Cummington proposes a work-study environment created specifically for the investigation of the unknown in art.

As the school progressed, it added to this brief rationale its own stance toward the role of the audience. In the theatre of "mixed means" [1] one does not lend one's presence unless one expects to participate, that is, to become *physically* involved with the occasion. Such engagement may include any stratagem the director or

[1] The intermedia movement is as yet too young to be burdened by its own rhetoric. As a result, it is referred to in various ways, depending upon the aesthetics of the one doing the talking. Richard Kostelanetz, therefore, reflects his own interests in the drama in the title of his book, *The Theatre of Mixed Means* [The Dial Press, 1968]. Others have referred to it as "mixed media," "action theatre," "Total Theatre," "Kinetic Environments," and "staged" or "pure" Happenings.

artist feels is appropriate to destroy the traditional passivity of the spectator. This coalition of performer and spectator was consistent with every activity that was planned and carried out at the Center.

What the Center offered, and subsequently provided, was a core of professionals already committed to intermedia who provided an energy center to the teen-agers, teachers, and college and art students who attended. One might describe the total school body as an enclave of malcontents, of art majors who spent much of their time in the drama department; of drama majors who were curious about filmmaking; of relatively untrained minds responding to the general "Geist" of their generation with a vague desire to say something of their own through the arts. The students came from colleges and art schools as distant as California and as close as Northampton; the faculty from such institutions as Brandeis, Harvard, the Philadelphia College of Art, Smith College, the Massachusetts College of Art, and the University of Massachusetts. A breakdown of the staff by function is as follows: actress, director, playwright, and a specialist in dramatic games; a still and film photographer and a film historian, a dancer-architect, and a composer of electronic music; a light designer and sculptor. Visiting lecturers came from such areas as computer sculpture, documentary films, and environments. (There were others scheduled, but the school requested that field trips and guest lectures be canceled so that they might attend to more important matters. This suggestion, which was made during the end of the third week, reflected a growing impatience with lectures or "presentations" of any sort that structured the group into the role of passive spectators.)

By the end of the third week we found we were working in four somewhat distinct domains:

1) The media area, which may be described as those activities that evolve out of such communications "hardware" as cameras, tape recorders, theatrical lighting, and projected images. It is difficult to state the case for the use of media as art without noting the role of Marshall McLuhan in the construction of a theoretical basis for its use. In an address to the International Center for the Communication in Arts and Sciences, McLuhan stated [2] (among other things): ". . . sensory levels have already changed drastically since TV. The visual component in our lives has dropped dramatically, and the visceral, kinetic, and auditory modes of responses have risen to compensate." In short, the desire of young people to explore the technology of their age as a means of expression may be viewed as an *inevitable sensory shift, capable of altering not only the artist's expression but the public views of entertainment as well.*

2) An interpersonal awareness area that arose out of the "games," improvisations, and dance exercises, and that reflected activities of the human potential movement of the Esalen Institute of California, "T" groups, and other confrontation techniques. William Shutz, currently a leading exponent of the movement, puts it this way: "Joy is the feeling that comes when one realizes his potential for feeling, for having inner freedom of openness, for full expression of himself, for being able to do whatever he is capable of, and for having satisfying relations with others and with society. How is joy attained? A large part of the effort, unfortunately, must go into undoing guilt, shame, embarrassment, or fear of punishment, failure, success, retribution—all must be overcome." [3] *The "awareness" idea fulfills a need for people of all ages, not only to "level" with themselves but*

[2] Vision '68 Conference, Southern Illinois University.
[3] William Shutz, *Joy: Expanding Human Awareness* (New York: Grove Press, 1967), p. 20.

to take some action against the numerous debilitating effects of social hypocrisy. Young people, in a sense, are telling us that time is running out, and if we are finally to be honest with each other, we must begin with ourselves.

3) A linking area of happenings, episodes, celebrations, and rituals, which could draw from, or combine, either of the preceding two areas in the planning of "events" that were temporary in nature and designed to involve the entire school as participants. It is safe to say that at least ninety percent of our evenings were devoted to such occasions, with both faculty and students assuming leadership in the designing of programs.

4) The fourth domain, although occupying an admittedly minimal position, fulfilled the need of students to achieve personal satisfaction through more traditional art forms—namely, painting, potting, and sculpting. A kiln was built; large environmental structures appeared on hillock and meadow; and occasionally a painting appeared—on easel, on wall, or, in the most dramatic case, a huge Pop figure that totally changed the character of the barn.

A brief sampling of activities taken from the above will demonstrate the limitations of conventional classification.

—A series of group improvisations that ultimately led to the realization that the group was dealing with the murder scene in *Macbeth*. The exercise, which finally ended with a crescendo of improvised light, sound, and movement, was carried out against the script as originally written.

—A midnight ritual on a mountaintop involving choral verse reading and the symbolic burning of huge wooden effigies symbolizing forces of constriction in our past. The second half of the activity was built upon

Object—Cummington, Massachusetts

positive aspects of familial relationships and concluded with a fruit and wine ceremony.

—A twelve-hour "time-lock" where time was "framed" and the group was forced to confront each other in a variety of ways.

—The creation of a multimedia play written with actors, dancers, sound, light, and film equipment at the playwrights' immediate disposal. This was an ongoing "event" that lasted for daily afternoon sessions for a two-week period.

—The "raku" [tea] ceremony rewritten in contemporary terms, with a gas-fired kiln built for the occasion.

—A Saturday night party to celebrate the arrival of light, board, and dimmer equipment; the workshop turned into a forest with stage settings and backgrounds for projected images.

—The workshop was converted into a series of levels, broken into segments by parachutes and yards of plastic. Participants moved on cue like chessmen as the playwright dictated moves that were related to a parable. Strobes and projections, both still and moving, were incorporated into the action.

—An environment created for play and poetry readings, participants seated formally on either side of rows of fluorescent tubes with pews and lights swathed in boughs of evergreen.

—Environmental exercises included reconversion of student living areas, repainting the barn with Pop symbols, the construction of large-scale wood sculpture, and a complex junk structure built around the school bell.

—A taped composition written for an electronic light board.

Bart Hayes, coming in advance of the trustees, was impressed by "conceptual approaches which go beyond specialized skills." He reported positively to the trustees who then participated in the program and voted to con-

tinue the idea the following summer. There were reservations and suggestions for improvement, but basically
the reaction was positive. The following fall, however,
the trustees had second thoughts and voted to abandon
this concept of an art school. This was understandable
and not unexpected as an intermedia operation can be
a hairy experience for someone unaccustomed to the
language and personal style of the participants. My co-
director, Arthur Hoener, and I both recognized the possibility of the cultural shock that might result from a
confrontation of trustees and a turned-on situation. Since
we ran the operation along democratic lines, Arthur and
I were unable to curb what appeared to be certain ex-
cesses of behavior and which eventually worked against
the life of the center. There is a certain obsolescence
factor built into any controversial operation that draws
its support from establishment sources. In other words,
it's tough for an administrator to go all the way without
getting himself killed off in the process. This is the
"Kamikaze" approach to innovation which, although
hazardous, is not without its merits.

PERSONAL OBSERVATION

There were very definite stages of involvement that
were noted throughout the five-week period. Initiative
was taken primarily by those with the most skills: that
is, the staff began most of the projects, drawing in the
younger ones as assistants. This created some competi-
tion between the stronger leaders and was followed by
a second, or regrouping, stage. The inexperienced and
untrained "shopped" for the most exciting projects; in
some cases there was a great deal of "rapping," looking
off into space, fooling with guitars, and running off to
the swimming hole. The high school group was at a
distinct disadvantage in initiating projects and in at

least two instances, dropouts decided to return to school and get the diploma that would enable them to get the skills they wanted at college and art schools.

Very little of the content of the projects bore any relationship to the soothing, pastoral environment of the school's mountaintop location. Students generally brought their "hang-ups" with them, using these as a source of ideas. Thus, one hypothesis would seem to have been verified: namely, that the intermedia movement is an urban phenomenon, serving as a fresh vehicle of expression for the frustrations of race, war, and social imbalance of all kinds.

Artistic expression is now valid as a *group process* as well as an individual concern. Dialogue therefore can exist among several artists as well as between an individual painter and his canvas.

In sponsoring intermedia programs, there is still a need to consider criteria ("How do you know it works?") as well as content ("What are you saying?"). Much of the content of intermedia currently rests on either end of a tired seesaw, with social protest sitting on one end, and a mindless, formless state of psychedelic euphoria on the other. Both ends are in process of settling into patterns, which, in their own way, are as formalized as the strictures imposed by the academies of another era. We must encourage students to explore the fruitful middle ground in the hope that we may begin to deal with some positive aspects of the human condition.

No one should embark on any role in intermedia if he is unsympathetic to the apparently antisocial conduct of youth or if he is easily threatened by seemingly bizarre and egocentric behavior. Avoid intermedia if you see yourself as an "authority" figure or if you don't know how to listen. Don't get involved if you are afraid of criticism of outsiders, if you need a blueprint for the

future, and if you place no trust in the unknown. Intermedia, like any art form, is not for the timid, nor is it
to be undertaken lightly.

For people who eschew being "lectured at" and who
prefer images to words, some of the most articulate
youth of our time may be found in the intermedia
movement.

We have always known that art is life, the difference
now being that in our time art is politics, and politics,
in turn, veers toward the left. (This may account for
the paucity of conservative folk singers.) The restructuring of form within the visual arts is only one part
of the fusion that is taking place in the arts of performance; and the intermedia movement, now achieving an identity of its own, is a process that binds younger
artists to an older generation, minimizing artistic to
social concerns. Artists thus seem to have brought to a
head the paradox of the artist as described by Virgil
Aldrich, "On the one hand the artist seems remote from
life, caught in the self-sufficiency of his works of art and
not knowing how to live, really; yet on the other, he
seems to be more intimate than nonartists are with life
so that he can reveal its secret." [4] The secret, for the
present, at least, would seem to be in at least two arenas,
the political and the aesthetic.

[4] Virgil Aldrich, *Philosophy of Art* (Englewood Cliffs, New Jersey:
Prentice-Hall, Inc., 1963).

ENVIRONMENTAL AESTHETICS FOR TEACHERS OF ART *

Frederick M. Logan

. . . .

The decline of systems of mass transportation and the resultant emphasis on private vehicular movement were the first indications of a general decline that has affected all walks of life, according to Frederick M. Logan. He assumes "What pollutes the biological chain of life . . . must already have polluted our aesthetic sensibilities.

Logan points out that in order to get at the source of American aesthetic education "one must watch commercial television . . ." and he feels that the values and goals advocated on television are not practical even if they were possible. What he means is not difficult to imagine. Elsewhere in this book Les Levine points out: "television commercials are the real programming of television."

Art teaching and education can play a role in helping human beings to find humane and pleasant arrangements for living; indeed ". . . human beings have found many such arrangements, but few of them have yet found

* Reprinted from *Art Education* (October, 1970).

their way to the United States," he notes.
The author feels that the situation of the
teacher in well-to-do city schools is not hope-
less, because there still is the chance to in-
troduce ideas about new living patterns;
however, Logan admits that, for the ghetto
teacher, the situation is very different and
any presentation of new concepts requires a
different manner of exposition.

Frederick M. Logan is well known in art
education circles. He is Professor of Art Edu-
cation at the University of Wisconsin at Madi-
son, and author of Growth of Art in American Schools *(New York: Harper & Bros., 1955)*
as well as many articles. In 1964 he taught at
the School of Art Education in Birmingham,
England, and in 1968/69 was chief of the
Northern Nigeria Teacher Education Project.

. . . .

Beginning with the economic boom years of Post World
War II some scholars in the biological and sociological
fields have been warning us that our industrial and social practices were polluting the earth at a dangerous
rate. The continuance of a huge military arms establishment, combined with the production of consumer goods
to meet the backlog of demand piled up during war
years, more than offset any potential depression for a
high percentage of the white population. These circumstances, combined with the quiet discard of proposed
public-works projects, which had been developed to meet
the threat of widespread postwar unemployment, created a booming private enterprise economy. Not only
did the planned-for emergency government works projects prove "unnecessary" for the relief of unemployment,

but the largest government enterprise of all times, other than warfare, the interstate highway system, gobbled up the lion's share of tax money after the bare necessities were met in the way of keeping the federal establishment operating. Furthermore, the "I" system multiplied some of the most threatening of the polluting aspects of our overheated and relatively undirected industrial production. The electrical rapid-transit systems, built up to models of efficiency by 1920, and allowed to stagnate in the Depression of the thirties, were overloaded, and understaffed during war years to the disgust of the population generally.

With the coming of peace, the tremendous production of new cars and the "I" system, the private automobile crowded out the beat-up old rapid transit. Carbon dioxide went to work on the atmosphere, at first distressing no one but a few of the Cassandra-type scholars, and the returning GIs went into family life with the same wholehearted, productive enthusiasm. The schools have been multiplying available classrooms, while the highways and their auto populations have also been multiplying the linear and square miles given over to concrete, to interchanges, and to roadsides.

Now the bonanza period draws to a close. Deferred payments must be made. The enormous population of the United States, and the still larger proportionately multiplied population of the earth, has, somehow, to be educated to the finite quality of earthly resources. Air is not free. Water is not free. Space is not limitless. All that the earth has to offer will run out, and soon, at the present rate of heedless gobbling up of metals, oil, trees, even soil itself. The air and water, from being the most beneficent of God-given resources, can be made, by man, into worldwide poisons. An impressive start has been made toward that goal.

What pollutes the biological chain of life, what disjoints and pollutes our social communities, must already have polluted our aesthetic sensibilities. And it has; we are so aesthetically polluted that the very basis of our reaction to the biological social problems of pollution is dreadfully misguided and false at the core.

To get at the source of American aesthetic education one must watch commercial television and read the consumer advertisements in the newspapers. For the affluent American middle class, the weekly and monthly magazines are also potent aesthetic educators. And the upper middle class is in a financial position to accomplish some of its aesthetic dreams, such as they have become. As a result, their houses, their furniture, their clothing, their vacation homes, their travels are the models for the unrealized dreams of less affluent city dwellers, and of the dispossessed drifting population of the ghettos. And the jet set, the all-out international tax dodgers, the rare jewel bargainers, the residents of costly estates separated from urban crowds and ugliness by miles of water or thousands of acres serve as the ultimate in aesthetic aspiration. As yet, there are no alterations in the public mind to this pinnacle of the good life. The college-age revolt from middle-class values, epitomized by this group, has reacted strongly against the primness of the suburbs, the conformity of the middle-class garb and life patterns, but their alternatives are not yet clear. Let us see what teachers of art might ponder upon as their contribution to clarity.

What aesthetic values do we see that do, or can, stand out against the aesthetic pollution we experience in the environment? Agreement as to the nature of the pollution must come before agreement, or even tentative suggestions for counteraction, can be proposed.

I believe we can assume that the biological need for

reversing water, air, and soil pollution practices must come ten times faster than our present national and state governments appear to believe. The cumulative effects of continued local and worldwide stupidity in this regard will, at best, take generations to overcome and to correct. Aesthetically, pure lakes and streams, and unpoisoned air cannot be argued against. Also, since dirty oceans, dirty lake water, dirty air, and infected soil are now proven to be pervasive, affecting the health of every earthly inhabitant, rich and poor alike, we shall soon have to learn the importance of taking vast corrective measures. The rich and the well-to-do must support the effort as, in the nineteenth century, they supported the efforts to eliminate the great plagues.

But the "establishment" of art and of art education will not be a leading force in that basic task.

Our basic task may be that of projecting an aesthetically tolerable environment for three or four hundred million people, which can be well under construction in the rest of this century. That environmentally sound continental home should be predicated on the basis of a society in which every family has a place, a socially worthwhile task to perform, an expectation of a decent life in exchange. If we give this objective a little thought we see that the aesthetic environmental aspirations of the present day are not only false, they are potentially self-defeating, because they cannot be achieved without deepening and complicating the deterioration of the biological and sociological system.

Television creates a dream pattern of each family secure in its own multibedroom house on its own plot of half an acre or more, reached by curving tree-shaded streets where there are no traffic-clogged highways, no billboard jungles, no slums, no decaying retail streets, no factories, and where schools are set in beautiful parklike surroundings; Mommy drives the latest station wagon,

Daddy goes off to work in some unknown but cheery place, and whenever the family encounters the big outside world they arrive all bright and gay in a smart restaurant, an airport, out in the country, without ever seeing anything dull, depressing, dirty, brutish, or just plain boring. In a carefully limited sense, life on the boob tube is beautiful for middle-class America. For good measure these days and to prove that television has a social conscience, a carefully laundered, not very black child is slipped into the background occasionally.

Life is not like that, even for middle-class white America.

Life cannot be like that ever, for anybody. It is an aesthetic, nostalgic, dream of existence for millions of Americans, but it can only be a schizophrenic delusion. Even the rapidly growing crop of millionaires cannot truly achieve such an unsullied paradise by the purchase of hideaways in the metropolitan towers or recreational retreats in wilderness areas. Recently we read that Thor Heyerdahl found a thousand miles of ocean littered with oily crusts; and the whine of the jet aircraft together with the racket of the helicopter is no respecter of wilderness or wealth. To borrow Bradley's title for his book on the atomic bomb, there is "no place to hide."

Aesthetic aspirations for our communally shared environment can deal only with the costly, but stimulating possibilities of making over what we have. Not only is Frank Lloyd Wright's Broadacre City minimum of one acre per family not economically possible, it is proving socially sterile where the well-to-do have been able to afford it.

We live in cities now, more of us than ever before. We resent the crowding, the noise, the polluted air, the chemically treated water, the deteriorating city services, the lack of sympathetic neighborhood police protection since traffic duties have overwhelmed police departments.

Aesthetically, there remain many possibilities for the good life in large and middle-sized cities. In American cities there are thousands of square miles of single- and double-family houses on reasonably sized lots that are comfortable, not too costly, and can be maintained to suit the tastes of the residents. Two- to four-story apartment units are not as plentiful, but they exist in some numbers in good states of repair. Land covered with residential structures once decent, but now derelict beyond economically sound rehabilitation, also exists in large and small cities.

If the art teacher talks with students enough to know their hopes for a life-style of their own, he finds that most individuals crave occasional privacy and most individuals want to be clean and to live physically cleanly. After that, they crave a good life in terms of the popular television fantasies.

Here is the point of departure for the art teacher who has begun to look at and think about the environment. The spacious house on private grounds, miles away from urban noise and dirt, and deep in tree shade, is not an attainable life goal for all American people, or indeed, even for a substantial minority of them. The use of the privately owned vehicle, two or three to a family, even if its power source were less of a polluter than the combustion engine, would disrupt every other human activity if we all had to have it to go to and from our homes to distant work, school, and shopping places.

Human beings must find humane and pleasant arrangements for living closer together than our present overrated suburban scheme. As a matter of fact, human beings have found many such arrangements, but few of them have yet found their way to the United States. Not only are there alternative ways for creating fine homes for families needing them, but also there are architects capable of developing specific proposals for developing old parts of cities by refurbishing existing housing and introducing into old neighborhoods the kind of open space that human beings crave. Open space that goes on and on and on, with trees and grass and pools of water, and running brooks, where roads go over one's head because bridges are large enough to provide a walk space underneath, and where from time to time a grassy area appears where games are played and benches for casual watchers are nearby—open space like that is what New York's Central Park was meant to be. But space like that for each separate family is not to be. Space like that even in the suburbs is seldom found, except along state-owned parkways or in State Park reservations. The suburbanite, in fear that his private heaven will be intruded upon by outsiders, makes his own plot of ground larger and votes against public parkland. By that process he denies the teen-ager of the suburbs the same privilege of exploration on bike or on foot that the center-city child is also denied.

Aesthetically, city, suburb, small town, and countryside need the publicly owned and publicly cherished open spaces. They are needed for our relaxation and enjoyment. They are needed in large enough areas so that individuals and small groups can use them with a degree of privacy. They are needed to enhance residential neighborhoods that have been on the way to final demolition by way of neglect.

The aesthetic quality of the environment is just as dependent upon the economic structure of the nation as have been the arts of painting, sculpture, and the graphic arts. Museums in the United States hit the jackpot with the Internal Revenue ruling that gifts of art to public museums could be claimed as deductions from one's income tax. This is not the place to go into the details of the ruling. Suffice it to point out that it has been generous enough to attract the attention of many wealthy persons whose previous art interests were minimal.

The aesthetic qualities of urban and suburban environment will not be measurably improved without similar tax advantages. Today, a decaying, neglected property in the ghetto is more valuable to its owner, in the long run, than a well-maintained building. Today, an old, mixed neighborhood of residences, small business, and many small retail establishments may be the home neighborhood of a lively, but relatively low-income group of families. The tax structure, rather than favoring the preservation of such a neighborhood, introducing into it or near it, needed open space, encouraging do-it-yourself building improvements, is more likely to force it into decay. City health, school, and police services will be allowed to deteriorate. Taxes will discourage good maintenance. Finally, land prices for industrial projects, for unwanted "slum" clearance, will be subsidized by local or federal government agencies, and the once quietly improving neighborhood becomes a ghetto on the way to being "redeveloped."

Art teachers are not usually tax experts, or real estate consultants. Besides that, it is doubtful that they are ready to teach these relationships adequately. They can be aware, however, that aesthetic community changes are economic in origin, and that community projects call for capital investment private or public and for economic inducements to maintain and improve property.

In the schoolroom and for the art teacher what does all this mean? In the ghetto classroom, perhaps nothing, directly. In the face of prevailing hopelessness brought on by lack of work and by the civic neglect of ghetto neighborhoods, some messages of hope from the teacher may sound miserably out of place. To suggest imaginative drawings, paintings, and models of what their neighborhood might be could invite a classroom disaster or a round of hysterical jocularity. Art teachers in some schools have to write their own curricula, be their own psychologists, draw their own sociological data and conclusions and, finally, tune their own pedagogical and aesthetic wavelengths to be received by their particular audience in that school, in that city. This paper can suggest only that art teachers seek information about the enormous possibilities of decent city environments for all kinds of people and incomes, that they follow local developments and interpret these to their students on the basis of their own judgment. To free children of tinsel dreams at best only third rate, as well as technically impossible, one is obliged to help them to form more interesting dreams.

For the teacher in the well-to-do city wards, and in the suburbs, the situation is different. His students are physically comfortable. Their expectations in the world may be modest, or ambitious, but they have reasonable hopes of achieving them. They are not by any means noticeably satisfied with their parents' way of life and thus are interested in other points of view. The city as it is, and as it could become, is unknown to many of them. They have been conditioned to stay out and away. They are highway children for shopping, snacking, moviegoing, and dating. They are ignorant, for the most part, of cultural centers, the central library, theatre, music, museums, and art galleries. Few of them have encountered the notion that inner-city living could be much more satisfying for some of them than suburban living.

A structure of expanding urban life, which would call for more compactly grouped homes within easy distance of public open space, which, in itself, should be almost endless, like parkways, now narrow and then again broad in expanse—this idea would be foreign to nearly all their preconceptions. But they would come upon such a new idea with an easier feeling of possible achievement than would the ghetto child.

On second thought, it is doubtless morally wrong to assume that the child who suffers social and civic neglect cannot begin to see what a better, and yet still more urban, world can be. Perhaps all that need be different is the manner of its exposition. He needs to see it as a goal to be legitimately claimed. The suburban child needs to see that, for all his physical comforts, the suburb has shortchanged him, too. He needs the city that American life can make every bit as much as, perhaps in certain ways even more than, the child of the ghetto—the ghetto that has for too long a time been an expensive luxury to the city and a criminal waste of life to its residents.

Little concern with self-expression in art media has been indicated here. With that aspect of art experience I believe art teachers have done very well. When school has been left behind, individuals who have been stimulated by their work in art classes can and do reflect that interest in the places in which they live. One's private environment can at all times and in all places be a personal expression of one's way of life, which refreshes the mind.

But human beings seek community as well as privacy. Teachers of art, in their concern for better aesthetic environment, had better tear themselves loose from the suburbia of house-and-garden magazines to start their education in a greater range of urban alternatives in the pattern of life that we must construct. We can have beautiful cities with decent homes for all. We can preserve the countryside from ill-conceived costly suburban sprawl. We can have open space in city and country open to all. These virtues are not only possible to us, they are very likely essential for us to build. Because without the successful re-creation of our urban centers, we are also probably doomed to fail in striking the ecological balances that we know are absolute requirements.

Louis Sullivan's "Form follows function" has never been so imperative. What the function of our man-made environment must be is emerging more clearly every day. The forms we develop to meet that function will be wonderfully various. Teachers of art should be busier than most in projecting ideas about the forms of our communal future.

REFERENCES

Ian L. McHarg, *Design with Nature* (New York: The Natural History Press, 1969). Paul Shepard and Daniel McKinley, eds., *The Subversive Science*. Essays Toward an Ecology of Man (New York: Houghton Mifflin Co., 1969). Wolf Von Eckardt, *A Place to Live* (New York: Delacorte Press, 1967).

Gregory Battcock (center) at the John Weber Gallery with John Weber (left) and Simone Swan (right). Photograph by David Bourdon.

AN EXPERIMENT WITH ART
IN EDUCATION *

Gregory Battcock

. . . .

It doesn't take a student (or police) riot to tell you that
something may be wrong with current teaching practices
in the liberal arts; the contradictions and distortions have
been apparent for years. The problem is especially difficult in art because it looks as though we're doing the
right thing because we seem to be getting acceptable results. Of course, student dissension remains, and art itself
is all too often ignored.

We teach design by showing students examples of good
design, yet somehow (thanks to our Abstract-Expressionist heritage) design gets separated from meaning and is
conveniently disassociated from larger social and ethical
issues that, after all, are what really comprise the culture.
We imply, at best, that good design might even prove a
remedy for contemporary social and cultural crises while
we know that, in fact, it's quite impossible.

The experiment described in this paper does not pretend to seek results in the conventional sense. We were
not particularly concerned with good design or professional technique. Perhaps these don't really belong in an
art classroom in the first place—though contemporary developments in art may reveal that, after all, they are a
concern of art.

* Reprinted from *Art Education,* Vol. 24, No. 1 (January, 1971).

The experiment intended to show that good art and good design must primarily be social matters that can be pragmatically evaluated. We hoped to indicate that art can be socially directed and maintain its integrity in the service of a social and cultural revolution. The weaknesses in its design, methodology, and even interpretation are readily admitted by the author. Indeed the only clearly demonstrable fact concerning the experiment is that it was an awful lot of fun for everybody involved.

An investigation into the subtleties of the Abstract-Expressionist aesthetic may reveal that it was indeed an elitist art system, which, though philosophically essential, was antisocial and thus antihumanitarian as well. If so, it would seem that art schools should abandon those procedures, techniques, attitudes, and goals that are dependent upon Abstract-Expressionist principles. Instead they should seek out new, more immediate relationships with developments in contemporary art. And that seems to be a problem. In the notes that follow I should like to suggest an "alternate" method that may lead to a more authentic involvement for visual art with the liberal educational process.

ART AND EDUCATION DON'T OVERLAP

All the lengthy research papers, the doctoral dissertations, the "artistic" experiments, and the art education symposia in the world will not bring art and education into a positive, active relationship unless some of the basic principles of art are a lot better understood. As a matter of fact, such endeavors may tend to strain whatever didactic connections exist between education and art. In the end we should not be surprised to learn that art and art education are two vastly different phenomena that operate at cross-purposes—as communicative systems frequently do. In this case, unfortunately, education tends to absorb energy while art seems to actuate it.

CAN WE FORGET ABOUT GETTING RESULTS?

The seventies will be the decade for the art critics; they will have their day. But it won't matter, because art criticism is still art's greatest calamity. So is art education. If the art critics don't succeed in destroying art, the art educators will. Both claim a similar "academic" authority. Art criticism, as we know it and as the Abstract Expressionists wanted it, is hopeless. But the fact remains that as long as we insist upon getting results in art education, we cannot achieve authentic art learning. Art education as a productive discipline must fail; it cannot possibly produce legitimate, strong art. As a matter of fact, it can't produce anything. Art education is a broad discipline that cannot have anything to do with specifics. Art unifies—provides the lineaments—for the entire environment, including the physical, social, and philosophical worlds.

What this means is that art education is quite finished, whether we know it or not. What it also means is that we are on the threshold of an art education that may finally assume a positive role that does not negate art itself.

WHY ARTISTS HATE ART

Contemporary activity in art has been labeled by critics and philosophers "anti-art." The new art style is a logical reaction to traditional, capitalistic principles in art and, as such, may be even more difficult to understand than some previous styles of the avant-garde. The mainstream of Western artistic tradition appears to many artists today as providing for the accommodation of established culture—therefore it is not acceptable, and artists have devised numerous ways to circumvent it. As a result it is more difficult now than ever before for art educators to recognize authentic contemporary developments in art.

However, unless they do so, we probably will never be able to establish a new sensorium (combination of receptive and critical faculties). It can only be created by existent faculties, and these aren't in such good shape, for they have been thoroughly distorted by the prevailing social condition. Herbert Marcuse has pointed out that the sensibility and the reason of man have been shaped by the order and organization of a class society—which have also shaped the freedom of the imagination. Conclusion: the power of the imagination has been repressed. Thus a new sensibility, a sensibility of freedom ". . . cannot develop in an environment shaped by and for aggressive impulses . . ."

How then can we in art establish a motivation free of the so-called aggressive impulses?

FREEDOM FROM AGGRESSIVE IMPULSES

The experiment in art education described in these notes was devised with a major goal of eliminating (as much as possible) aggressive impulses connected with the making of art. (The experiment was conducted with non-art majors. If art students enrolled in the B.F.A. program had been involved, no doubt the results would have been different. The students were not well informed about recent developments in art. Fortunately, the curriculum for the course was vague, and instructors were encouraged to innovate freely. Obviously the experiment could not occur under firm curriculum requirements.)

Recent developments in contemporary art—sometimes termed Conceptual art, "street works," and "anti-art" have insisted upon vague and subtle manipulations of man-made or natural environmental phenomena that sometimes result in art documents that are barely distinguishable from the ordinary environment. An artist may dig a hole in the woods, for example. Or he may submit a road map upon which he has indicated certain locations. One artist spilled some water on the rug at a gallery. Another has sent radio signals through the Connecticut air. John Perreault has organized loosely structured "street works" and has sought virtually anonymous co-operation by artists and nonartists. One of his artists meditated while standing on a street corner (Vito Acconci). Another, critic Scott Burton, fell asleep at an art opening. Hannah Weiner sought out a psychiatrist who had the same name, one Sunday afternoon on Fifth Avenue.

All the above were offered as serious artworks by serious artists. Some are silly; others deeply disturbing. They share in common a respect for the natural tools and supplies of the environment, which are manipulated, juxtaposed, arranged, and abused according to broad, loosely defined standards of good taste, dignified presentation, and, in general, artistic integrity. They rarely require special skills, and that's important. An artist could present an intelligent, provocative work and not know how to draw a straight line, mix colors, or stretch a canvas. It's also important that usually no "object" remains to be dealt with later. The work cannot be marketed, saved, or possessed in a conventional sense. The notion of monument in art has been subverted, and it's about time. The capitalistic economic marketplace, which itself has posed perhaps the greatest threat to the integrity of art in our society, has been bypassed. So have the roles of traditional institutions in art been circumvented. Of considerable importance is the shift in the role of the ego in art production. Visual artworks that are nonvisual, that are indistinguishable from the real environment, or that perhaps never really occurred, go a long way in denying much of the ego satisfaction that is sometimes a major, though questionable motivation in art.

The most extreme proposals by artists working in the new style seem to involve no actual work, other than the proposals themselves. The works described below are mostly confined to statements that were, however temporarily, actually resolved.

METHODOLOGY

The students concerned were lectured to about developments in modern art, and their social implications. They were introduced to some of the principles of Hegelian thought and to some of the art and cultural pronouncements of Marcuse. Many of the reasons for the new change in art emphasis and procedure were explained, though actual works were not discussed. Some of the students were unwilling to give up their beliefs (which were of a traditional nature), and others took to the idea like a duck to water. The major questions that were introduced challenged traditional notions, especially those that assume that visual artworks should be constructed from a limited range of materials and that they should possess several acceptable characteristics, such as portability, durability, and identification (expression) of the creator.

At first, the students were asked to design an artwork that they would *not* execute. Later on, each design was described to the group and the aesthetic merits, relationships to the natural and social environments, and possible literary interpretation were emphasized. Some works were criticized because they were too theatrical or contained primarily theatrical elements, others because they were almost pranks or fraternity initiation stunts. Thus

". . . setting up a barber chair and giving haircuts . . ." was not considered an appropriate idea.

Another student proposed that he inscribe a peace symbol, some thirty feet in diameter, with canned shaving cream sprayed upon a snow-covered hillside. The concept of applying visually similar textures was interesting. But why a peace symbol? Too much like a sign, and distracting as well. Finally a simple circle was decided upon. Ultimately the students agreed that perhaps the best way to realize the problem and heighten its meaning was simply to squirt the cream onto the snow in an ordinary, mushy pile.

The projects described herein were executed in the dead of winter, and the snow-covered ground accounts for the peculiar design and impact of many of the works. A young lady obtained a bushel of dead leaves and dumped them on the snow. She expected the wind to scatter the leaves around, and to some extent, it did. Therefore she built in a certain changeability that was in keeping with the major premise for the experiment.

WIT, OUTRAGE, AND MYSTERY

A white clothesline was tied from a fir tree to a No Parking sign some forty feet away. Unless seen against a dark background, the line was quite invisible. The end of the rope casually dangled down from the sign. We decided to label these works "campus works," and a good campus work was not supposed to draw attention to itself unnecessarily. The placement of the rope was hotly debated because, at first, it was decided to set it up someplace that would impede pedestrian traffic. For obvious reasons that idea was dropped and the more subtle and less obvious location was chosen.

Some works required rather complicated preparation, such as the case of the vanishing tree. A student arrived all prepared to paint a small scrawny tree, growing there all by itself, with a white solution that ". . . would be good for the tree." I insisted, mistakenly, that he get permission first. After wasting hours, explaining the reasons for painting the tree to various college officials, we ended up without permission, sympathy, or thanks. Finally I permitted the dejected and disillusioned student just to go and quietly paint the tree, which he did. The tree is still alive, and the white solution has finally worn off. Naturally nobody ever seemed to notice that the tree had been painted in the first place. The sight of the little tree, sitting there all by itself, almost totally invisible in the snow, was a delight and satisfaction for those involved.

Yet another work also involved a tree, but in quite a different way. After a lot of discussion, a tired, brownish shade of heavy wool was tangled up and tossed into the branches of a tree. It took three tries to get it up there, but it remained, all tangled up, blowing around in the branches for weeks before it finally, and not regretfully, disappeared.

ACCIDENTAL RESEMBLANCE TO NEW ART

Obviously many of the works executed by the students resembled works of art that were being proposed and executed by avant-garde artists; yet the students were certainly not familiar with these artists or their art. Therein lies perhaps one of the most interesting results of the experiment. Raphael Ferrer was dumping ice and leaves in the Whitney Museum; at the same time a student, acting independently, decided to do the same thing in the lobby of a classroom building. In Paris in November, 1969, Robert Ryman was pasting up blank sheets at the Yvon Lambert gallery; simultaneously, unknown to us all, a student was tearing down pieces of paper that had been pasted up on the walls of a corridor.

Ryman's art was putting the things up; the student's art was tearing them down.

The reasons for such remarkable similarities are not difficult to discover. Mainly the students were introduced to some of the same motivating concepts that professional artists were concerned with. Given the nature of the anti-art aesthetic to which professional artists are committed, the fact that students who know next to nothing about art but when properly motivated can produce works that are virtually undistinguishable from serious "art" can be seen as a confirmation of the legitimacy of the works offered by the professionals.

A recent exhibition designed by Seth Siegelaub and Michel Claura in Paris entitled "18 Paris IV. 70" consists mainly of the catalogue, which contains typewritten and photographed documentation. The works proposed by the students involved in the art experiment also depended primarily upon typewriter and camera. Some of the works presented in "18 Paris IV. 70" were never executed; some of the works proposed by the students were not executed, or even intended to be executed.

Sometimes it was just as well . . . execution would not really have been justifiable. Take the case of the dirt and the hole. The proposal was discussed and modified continually. It had something to do with digging a hole in Vermont and transplanting the dirt from another hole that would be dug in New Jersey. We all profited enormously from the discussion and the resultant questions and problems. There was no reason for actually *doing* it however.

DISCUSSION AND PLANNING REPLACE DOING

As it turned out, the most interesting result of the project seems to have been the discussion and the development of ideas and concepts. A proposal that originally had something to do with pasting up papers on bulletin boards ended up with tearing them down. On another occasion we arrived to collect a quantity of wooden "horses" that we finally decided to arrange on a hilltop, but, to our dismay (and excitement), we found that the maintenance people had thrown the boards into a quite beautiful heap. Clearly we had stumbled upon a beautiful work, and it was decided to "document" it before rearranging the pieces according to our own carefully worked out arrangement, which had been determined only after endless discussion concerning the common function of the "horses," and the various facets of their "language." We had never considered dismantling them and tossing them in a heap in the corner, but because of our exhaustive approach to the function and shape of the objects, we were able to appreciate fully the "artwork" accidentally created by the maintenance department.

RESULTS

We did not set out to make art, but ended up producing works that closely paralleled contemporary works by artists. We anticipated failure and ended up failing. Without doubt, most of the students didn't really know what was going on. While they may have been driven to think (if not drink), the results cannot be measured. There is little reason to believe they actually learned anything about art.

On the other hand, the lesson could prove effective if it were not a single isolated incident in aesthetic education. Few (if any) subsequent educational experiences will reinforce the technique and attitude toward problem awareness and conceptualization that were the subjects of the experiment. It's probably only accidental that all this would occur in an art class. Very likely, at another time and place, the art classroom may not be the best arena for this subject.

The experiment generated considerable enthusiasm from the students. They seemed to enjoy the discussions enormously, and at times some had to be almost physically constrained from executing works prematurely. Conventional classroom motivation was held to a minimum, and repressive motivations—attendance and grading— were dispensed with entirely. The novelty of the experiment contributed toward its warm reception. Also, the humor, protest, and outrageous aspects were attractions.

In at least one way the experiment could be read as a huge success. The students responded to abstract problems in an extraordinarily professional and surprisingly sophisticated way. This showed, perhaps, that they were able to understand the larger social and cultural concepts in a way that would not have been readable in conventional verbal form. Thus the visual language seems to have been legitimately employed in a pragmatic and enjoyable manner.